ACID-BASE TITRATIONS IN NONAQUEOUS SOLVENTS

This book is a part of the
ALLYN AND BACON CHEMISTRY SERIES

Consulting Editors: DARYLE H. BUSCH
                      HARRISON SHULL

Acid–Base Titrations in Nonaqueous Solvents

James S. Fritz

Iowa State University

Allyn and Bacon, Inc.
Boston

CONTENTS

Preface

Titration is indeed a remarkable analytical technique. Acidic or basic components of a sample can be titrated quickly and accurately by using only the most rudimentary analytical equipment. And, several samples can be titrated completely and automatically in sequence with sophisticated modern instruments that also print out the results. Whether done very simply or with more complex equipment, acid–base titrations represent a valuable tool for chemists and other scientists.

Titration of acids and bases in nonaqueous solvents compares favorably with aqueous titrations in speed, accuracy, and convenience. Moreover, solubility of organic compounds is rarely a problem with nonaqueous solvents, and much weaker acids and based can be titrated than in aqueous solutions. The potential ranges attainable in organic solvents are often much greater than in water. This makes it possible to titrate each compound in a mixture to a separate end point, provided there are significant differences in acidic or basic strength. Finally, acid anhydrides, acid chlorides, and other reagents that are incompatible with water can sometimes be employed profitably in nonaqueous titrations.

The purpose of this book is to make available in a single source the essential theory, principles, and practical applications of nonaqueous acid–base titrations. No attempt has been made to give procedures for an extensive list of specific acids and bases. Such would be self-defeating because of the ever-changing nature of analytical problems that are encountered. Instead, our goal is to make the student or practicing scientist aware of the techniques available and the principles involved so that he can intelligently select conditions for a given titration by himself.

This book has been written concisely so that desired information can be located and read quickly. Although the text is well documented, no attempt has been made to list all published papers. Problems are included at the end of each chapter to assist students in checking their understanding of some of the points made in the chapter. In Chap. 8 detailed laboratory procedures are given for several of the most useful titration methods. Most of these procedures have been carefully checked in the author's own laboratory.

The author wishes to acknowledge the valuable assistance of Michael Arguello, Elizabeth Rogers, Willy Glover, Louise Goodkin, and Mary McHugh for performing many titrations and other experiments to test various concepts; Charles Burgett for checking several of the laboratory procedures; and Mark Seymour for developing an improved cell for coulometric titrations. He also thanks Robert Grob and Robert Larson, who read and commented on the manuscript.

James S. Fritz

CHAPTER 1

Introduction and Overview

Our titration method represents, we believe, a new departure in alkalimetry and is not only interesting from a theoretical standpoint but practically should become applicable to a large number of organic acids which hitherto it has not been possible to determine by titration.

This quotation from a paper published in 1910 by Folin and Wentworth[1] gives two good reasons for acquiring some knowledge of nonaqueous acid-base titrations: theoretical interest and practical utility. This early paper described a method for titration of fatty acids in solvents such as chloroform, carbon tetrachloride, benzene, or toluene with a sodium alkoxide titrant and phenolphthalein as the indicator. Unfortunately, the proposed method received little attention for many years.

Another significant early work is contained in a series of papers by Conant, Hall, and Werner[2-5], which appeared from 1927 to 1930. Conant *et al.* showed that organic amines give excellent end points when titrated in glacial acetic acid with a strong mineral acid such as perchloric acid. Even aromatic amines, which are too weakly basic to be titrated in water or the lower alcohols, were found to be titratable with sharp end points in acetic acid. However, this discovery also appears not to have been widely used in analytical laboratories for some years after its publication.

In 1948, Moss, Elliott, and Hall[6] developed a method that for the first time made it possible for phenols, which are quite weak acids, to be accurately titrated. These authors used ethylenediamine as the solvent and sodium aminoethoxide as the titrant. Beginning in 1950, Fritz and his students,[7-11] Pifer and Wollish,[12-14] Riddick,[15] and others published a number of methods for titrating a wide variety of weak acids and bases in nonaqueous solvents. This time the speed, accuracy, simplicity, and broad applicability of the technique caught the attention of scientists;

and titration of acids and bases in nonaqueous solvents gained wide acceptance.

A monograph by the present author,[16] published in 1952, summarized the work up to that time on nonaqueous acid-base titrations. More recently, books by Kucharsky and Safarik[17] by Huber,[18] and by Gyenes[19] have appeared. And, a number of textbooks and handbooks include sections or chapters on acid-base titrations in nonaqueous solvents. The Fundamental Annual Reviews in *Analytical Chemistry* catalog the significant developments concerning nonaqueous acid-base equilibria and titrations.

The remainder of this chapter provides a brief overview on the subject of nonaqueous titrations so that the more detailed chapters that follow may be read with a better perspective.

1.1   Titration of Bases

Scope

Under the proper conditions bases that are only slightly ionized in water (pK_b in H_2O = 10 or 11) may be titrated easily in a nonaqueous solvent; titration of somewhat weaker bases is possible using special techniques. Titratable compounds include aliphatic amines, basic nitrogen heterocyclics, aromatic amines, alkali metal and amine salts of most acids, and a wide variety of miscellaneous basic compounds. Mixtures of two or more bases that have significantly different basic strength in the nonaqueous solvent may be titrated with a separate end point for each base. Primary, secondary, and tertiary amines in mixtures may also be distinguished quantitatively using appropriate reagents to react with some of the amines.

Solvents

To permit titration of a weak base, the solvent should have as weakly basic properties as possible. The lower alcohols, like water, permit titration of medium strength bases such as aliphatic amines (pK_b in H_2O = 4–5), but these solvents are sufficiently basic that weak bases like pyridine (pK_b in H_2O = 8.8) and aniline (pK_b in H_2O = 9.4) cannot be titrated very well. Glacial acetic acid, however, permits an excellent titration of all of these and has been used extensively for titration of a wide variety of bases.

Because of its acidic properties many bases (B) react extensively with acetic acid (HAc) to form a new base, the acetate ion: (Ac⁻)

$$B + HAc \rightleftarrows BH^+ + Ac^-$$

Acetic acid is a leveling solvent because the bases, which may have different strengths, are leveled to the basic strength of the acetate ion. To avoid this, nearly neutral solvents such as acetone, acetonitrile, or nitromethane are sometimes used for the titration of bases. Bases at least as weak as aniline can be titrated accurately, and mixtures containing bases of different strength can be analyzed. For example, a mixture of aliphatic and aromatic amines titrated in one of these solvents with perchloric acid in dioxane gives two distinct end points, the first for the aliphatic and the second for the aromatic amines.

Titrants

For best results the titrant should be as strong an acid as possible. In aqueous solution the strong mineral acids (hydrochloric, hydrobromic, perchloric, nitric, etc.) serve equally well in this respect because each ionizes completely in water to give the same acid, H_3O^+. However, in acetic acid, which is less basic than water, these mineral acids exhibit considerable differences in acidic strength. Perchloric is the strongest acid and is therefore commonly used to titrate bases in acetic acid and other organic solvents. The titrant is prepared simply by dissolving the required amount of 70-72% perchloric acid, which is approximately $HClO_4 \cdot 2H_2O$, in glacial acetic acid. Usually a 0.01 M to 0.5 M titrant is used.

Sometimes it is desirable to exclude acetic acid from a titration system because of its leveling effect on mixtures of certain bases. In such cases perchloric acid in 1,4-dioxane is a good titrant and may be used for titrations in which the bases to be titrated are dissolved in almost any other solvent.

End-Point Detection

The end point in a nonaqueous titration of a base is usually detected either potentiometrically or visually with an acid–base indicator. Potentiometric detection is recommended for titration of weak bases that do not give sharp end points with visual indicators, and for mixtures that differ sufficiently in basic strength to give separate end points for each base.

Potentiometric titrations in most nonaqueous solvents can be performed very easily with a pH meter or other direct-reading titrimeter. The millivolt scale and not the pH scale of a pH meter should be used. Usually an ordinary glass indicator electrode is used in conjunction with either a fiber, porous plug, or sleeve-type calomel reference electrode.

A typical titration curve in acetic acid is illustrated in Fig. 1.1. Potentiometric titrations are satisfactory in all solvents except those of

3

very low dielectric constant, such as benzene, chloroform, dioxane, and other ethers. In these solvents the high electrical resistance makes stable potential readings difficult or impossible to obtain with ordinary equipment.

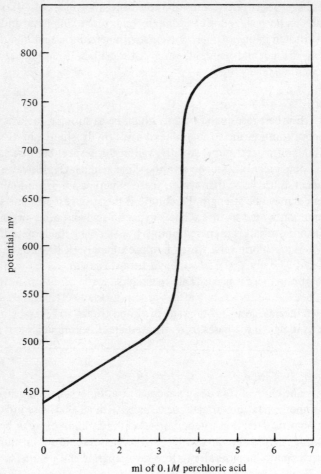

Figure 1.1 *Titration of aniline in glacial acetic acid with 0.1* M *perchloric acid, measured with glass-modified calomel electrodes [calomel filled with saturated* $(CH_3)_4NCl$ *in 2-propanol].*

Many indicators have been found for titration of bases in non-aqueous solvents. However, in acetic acid (and in several other solvents) crystal violet, or the closely related compound methyl violet, have been the most widely used. These indicators give a vivid and quickly reversible color change for titrations carried out in a wide variety of solvents. With increasing acidity, crystal violet changes from violet (its basic form) to green and finally to yellow. Frequently, blue, blue-green and yellow-green shades are also observed near the end point of a titration because of mixing the various forms of the indicator. Most bases can be titrated successfully if the first complete disappearance of a violet tinge is taken as the end point. However, it is advisable first to titrate each type of compound potentiometrically in order to select the correct end-point color.

1.2   Titration of Acids

Scope

Acids up to about pK_a in H_2O of about 11 may be titrated in nonaqueous solvents if the solvent and titrant are properly chosen. Many inorganic acids, organic sulfonic acids, carboxylic acids, enols, phenols, imides and several other structural types fall into this category. Many of these compounds are too weakly acidic to be titrated very well in water or alcohol-water mixtures. In nonaqueous solvents mixtures containing as many as five acids of different acidic strength have been resolved by a differentiating, potentiometric titration.

Solvents

Water, the lower alcohols, or a mixture of water and an alcohol is suitable for titration of a strong acid like hydrochloric or an organic sulfonic acid. Medium strength acids such as carboxylic acids (pK_a in H_2O = 4 to 5) may also be titrated fairly well in one of these solvents. However, titration of a weaker acid with a strong base titrant requires a solvent that is less acidic than water, methanol, or ethanol. Historically, the introduction of ethylenediamine[6] was an important breakthrough that permitted the titration of phenols so weakly acidic that their titration with a strong base had previously been impossible. Now, however, less basic solvents are more popular because they are easier to handle and do not level as many acids as ethylenediamine. Acetone, acetonitrile, t-butyl alcohol, dimethylformamide, 2-propanol, and pyridine may be used as the solvent for titration of strong, medium, or weak acids. 2-Propanol and solvent mixtures such as toluene-2-propanol[20] or ethylene glycol-hydrocarbon (G-H solvent)[21] are also useful, but the end point for titration of weak acids such as phenol is not as sharp as in the aforementioned solvents.

Titrants

Alcoholic potassium hydroxide is a satisfactory titrant for moderately weak acids. Various sodium and potassium alkoxides may also be used. However, a solution of sodium or potassium methoxide in benzene–methanol is a better titrant and serves well for the titration of acidic compounds in general. The methoxide titrant is prepared by reacting the alkali metal with methanol and diluting with benzene so that the benzene–methanol ratio would be 9, or 10 to 1. Benzene serves as an inert diluent for the titrant and reduces the amount of methanol added during the titration. This is important because methanol is acidic and reduces the sharpness with which weak acids can be titrated in a nonaqueous solvent if much methanol is present.

$$\text{base} \qquad \text{acid} \quad \text{base} \qquad \text{acid}$$
$$OMe^- + HA \rightleftharpoons A^- + MeOH$$
$$\text{(titrant)}$$

In the titration of most weak acids, results are improved markedly by titrating with methoxide in benzene–methanol instead of methoxide in methanol alone.

Nonaqueous solutions of tetrabutylammonium hydroxide or other quaternary ammonium hydroxides have at least two major advantages over other titrants. In almost every case the tetraalkyl ammonium salt of the titrated acid is soluble in the solvents commonly used. Sodium or potassium salts of titrated acids frequently form gelatinous precipitates. The other advantage of tetraalkylammonium hydroxides is that excellent potentiometric curves are obtained using ordinary glass and calomel electrodes. The "alkali" error limits the use of the glass electrode in conjunction with alkali metal alkoxide titrants, particularly in basic solvents. Methods of preparing quaternary ammonium hydroxide titrants are discussed in Chap. 4.

End-Point Detection

Titrations of acids in nonaqueous solution are usually followed potentiometrically, or the end point is detected by means of a visual indicator. For potentiometric titrations with tetraalkylammonium hydroxides a glass-calomel electrode system is generally used. The aqueous electrolyte in the calomel electrode is replaced with a saturated solution of potassium chloride in methanol, or with tetramethylammonium chloride in 2-propanol. Excellent titration curves for acids have been obtained in pyridine, acetone, acetonitrile, *t*-butyl alcohol, dimethylformamide and other solvents. A typical titration curve in dimethylformamide is shown in Fig. 1.2.

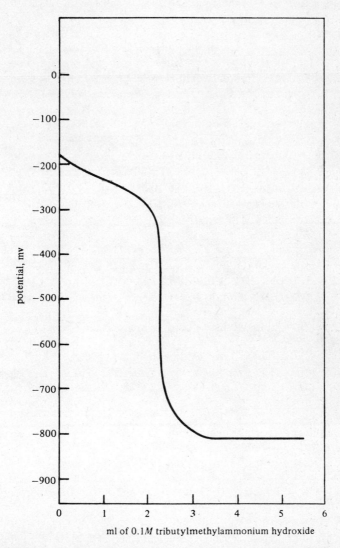

Figure 1.2 *Titration of benzoic acid in dimethylformamide with 0.1 M tributylmethylammonium hydroxide measured with glass-modified calomel electrodes.*

7

In acetonitrile,[22] t-butyl alcohol,[23] and pyridine[24] the approximate transition ranges of a number of indicators have been determined in terms of potentials measured with glass and calomel electrodes. Thus, if the potentiometric titration curve for any given compound is obtained, a satisfactory visible indicator can usually be selected.

REFERENCES

1. O. Folin and A. H. Wentworth, *J. Biol. Chem.*, **7** (1910), 421.

2. J. B. Conant and N. F. Hall, *J. Am. Chem. Soc.*, **49** (1927), 3047, 3062.

3. N. F. Hall and T. H. Werner, *Ibid.*, **50** (1928), 2367.

4. J. B. Conant and T. H. Werner, *Ibid.*, **52** (1930), 4436.

5. N. F. Hall, *Ibid.*, **52** (1930), 5115.

6. M. L. Moss, J. H. Elliott, and R. T. Hall, *Anal. Chem.*, **20** (1948), 784.

7. J. S. Fritz, *Anal. Chem.*, **22**, 578 1028 (1950), **24** (1952), 306, 674.

8. J. S. Fritz and N. M. Lisicki, *Ibid.*, **23** (1951), 589.

9. J. S. Fritz and R. T. Keen, *Ibid.*, **24** (1952), 308, 564; **25** (1953), 179, 407.

10. V. Vespe and J. S. Fritz, *J. Am. Pharm. Assoc.*, **41** (1952), 197.

11. J. S. Fritz and M. O. Fulda, *Anal. Chem.*, **25** (1953), 1837.

12. C. W. Pifer and E. G. Wollish, *Ibid.*, **24** (1952), 300.

13. C. W. Pifer, E. G. Wollish, *J. Am. Pharm. Assoc.*, (Sci. Ed.), **40** (1951), 609.

14. C. W. Pifer, E. G. Wollish, and M. Schmall, *Anal. Chem.*, **25** (1953), 310.

15. P. C. Markunas and J. A. Riddick, *Ibid.*, **24** (1952), 312.

16. J. S. Fritz, *Acid–Base Titrations in Nonaqueous Solvents*, Columbus, Ohio: G. F. Smith Chem. Co., 1952.

17. J. Kucharsky and L. Safarik, *Titrations in Nonaqueous Solvents*, Amsterdam: Elsevier, 1965.

18. W. Huber, *Titrations in Nonaqueous Solvents*, New York: Academic Press, 1967.

19. I. Gyenes, *Titration in Nonaqueous Media*, New York: Van Nostrand Reinhold Co., 1967.

20. L. Lykken, P. Porter, H. D. Ruliffson, and F. D. Tuemmler, *Ind. Eng. Chem., Anal. Ed.*, **16** (1944), 219.

21. S. R. Palit, *Ibid.*, **18** (1946), 246.

22. I. M. Kolthoff, M. K. Chantooni, and S. Bhowmik, *Anal. Chem.*, **39** (1967), 315.

23. L. W. Marple and J. S. Fritz, *Ibid.*, **35** (1963), 1305.

24. J. S. Fritz and F. E. Gainer, *Talanta*, **13** (1966), 939.

CHAPTER 2

Acid-Base Behavior in Nonaqueous Solvents

A knowledge of acid-base equilibria in various solvents leads to a better understanding of acid-base titrations in these solvents. In recent years the work of Kolthoff, Bruckenstein, Chantooni, Coetzee, and others has done much to elucidate various facets of acid-base behavior (especially, those pertaining to analytical applications) in solvents such as glacial acetic acid and acetonitrile. In this chapter acid-base behavior in four specific solvents of different properties will be discussed and compared. First, however, a few generalizations concerning acids, bases, and solvents will be mentioned.

2.1   Classification of Solvents, Acids, and Bases

Solvents may be divided into three general types.

1. *Amphiprotic.* This type undergoes self-ionization, or *autoprotolysis*, and has both acidic and basic properties. Autoprotolysis may be represented as follows:

$$2SH \rightleftharpoons SH_2^+ + S^- \qquad \text{general case}$$

$$2H_2O \rightleftharpoons H_3O^+ + OH^- \qquad \text{in water}$$

$$2CH_3OH \rightleftharpoons CH_3OH_2^+ OCH_3^- \qquad \text{in methanol}$$

$$2CH_3CO_2H \rightleftharpoons CH_3CO_2H_2^+ + CH_3CO_2^- \qquad \text{in acetic acid}$$

In each case the products of autoprotolysis are the solvated proton (sometimes written simply as H^+ or H_{SH}^+ for convenience) and the solvent anion, which is sometimes called the *lyate* ion. The auto-protolysis constant,

9

K_s, for the general case is defined as follows:

$$K_s = [SH_2^+][S^-]$$

2. *Nonionizable, with basic properties.* Examples of this type include ethers and pyridine. Ethers can react with an acid through the weakly basic oxygen, and pyridine through the basic nitrogen. Other than being weakly solvated, bases apparently do not react with this type of solvents.

3. *Aprotic, or inert.* This category includes solvents such as toluene, petroleum ether and carbon tetrachloride. Aprotic solvents do not interact with either acids or bases, except perhaps for weak solvation effects.

According to Brönsted's definition, an acid is any substance that can give up protons, and a base is any substance that can combine with protons. When an acid, HA, is dissolved in an amphiprotic solvent, SH, the resulting ionization is actually an acid–base reaction and increases the concentration of solvated protons, SH_2^+.

acid$_1$	base$_2$	acid$_2$	base$_1$	
$HA + SH$		$\rightleftharpoons SH_2^+$	$+ A^-$	general case
$HA + H_2O$		$\rightleftharpoons H_3O^+$	$+ A^-$	in water
$HA + CH_3OH$		$\rightleftharpoons CH_3OH_2^+$	$+ A^-$	in methyl alcohol
$HA + CH_3CO_2H$		$\rightleftharpoons CH_3CO_2H_2^+$	$+ A^-$	in glacial acetic acid

The extent of ionization depends on several things. One is the inherent acidity of HA. A strong acid, such as hydrochloric acid, is completely ionized in water, whereas a weak acid, such as acetic acid, is only slightly ionized. Another is the basic strength of the solvent. A basic solvent will promote ionization of an acid by virtue of an acid–base reaction with the dissolved acid. All the solvents listed above have some basic properties, although glacial acetic acid is a much weaker base than water, for example. Finally, the dielectric constant of the solvent, which is measure of the electrical insulating ability of the solvent, has an effect on ionization. Water has an unusually high dielectric constant, and in water ions are relatively free from attraction and repulsion effects (some effects do exist, as will be recalled from the difference between ionic concentration and activity in water). In most organic solvents, however, ions have a tendency to be present as *ion pairs* (cation–anion pairs). Thus, in glacial acetic acid solution even strong acids exist mostly as ion pairs, with very few *free* $CH_3COOH_2^+$ or A^- being present.

When a base is dissolved in an amphiprotic solvent, SH, the solvent acts as an acid and the resulting ionization increases the solvent anion concentration, S^-.

base$_1$ acid$_2$		acid$_1$ base$_2$	
B	$+ SH$	$\rightleftharpoons BH^+ + S^-$	general case
B	$+ H_2O$	$\rightleftharpoons BH^+ + OH^-$	in water
B	$+ CH_3OH$	$\rightleftharpoons BH^+ + CH_3O^-$	in methyl alcohol
B	$+ CH_3CO_2H$	$\rightleftharpoons BH^+ + CH_3CO_2^-$	in glacial acetic acid

The reaction of an acid and base in solution may well take place from the combining of solvated proton (due to ionization of the acid) and solvent anion (due to ionization of the acid):

$$HA + SH \rightleftharpoons SH_2^+ + A^-$$

$$B + SH \rightleftharpoons BH^+ + S^-$$

$$SH_2^+ + S^- \rightleftharpoons 2SH$$

The sum of these equations, however, is the simple Brönsted reaction

$$\text{acid}_1 \quad \text{base}_2 \quad \text{acid}_2 \quad \text{base}_1$$
$$HA + B \rightleftharpoons BH^+ + A^-$$

In type 2 solvents, acids also form a solvated proton. Because of the low dielectric constants of such solvents, the solvated proton exists primarily as an ion pair with the acid anion,

$$HA + S \rightleftharpoons SH^+A^-$$

A base, B, (which may be weakly solvated) reacts with the ion pair as follows:

$$SH^+A^- + B \rightleftharpoons BH^+A^- + S$$

This reaction occurs because B is a stronger base than the solvent, S.

In aprotic solvents an acid exists either as a molecular compound (HA) or as an undissociated ion pair (H^+A^-). These may be weakly solvated by the solvent. The acid can give up its proton to a base added to the aprotic solvent.

$$HA(\text{or } H^+A^-) + B \rightleftharpoons BH^+A^-$$

Another type of acid, known as a Lewis acid, does not give up protons. Lewis acids are molecules such as $AlCl_3$, BF_3 and $SnCl_4$ which have unfilled electron shells and react by accepting an electron pair from a base.

$$
\begin{array}{cc}
\text{acid} & \text{base}
\end{array}
$$

$$
\overset{\displaystyle F}{\underset{\displaystyle F}{F-B}} + \overset{\displaystyle R}{\underset{\displaystyle R}{:N-R}} \rightarrow \overset{\displaystyle F\;\;\;R}{\underset{\displaystyle F\;\;\;R}{F-B:N-R}}
$$

A Lewis acid can exist as such only in a nonionizable or aprotic solvent. In an amphiprotic solvent a Lewis acid will react with the solvent to form solvated protons. For example

$$AlCl_3 + 2H_2O \rightleftharpoons Al(OH)Cl_2 + H_3O^+ + Cl^-$$

Unlike most organic reactions and inorganic oxidation–reduction reactions, which proceed with measurable velocity, most acid–base reactions occur almost instantaneously. Lewis and Seaborg[1] noted that acids such as hydrogen chloride and boron trichloride react instantly with indicator bases even at $-70°C$. Several compounds were found which behaved like typical acids and bases except that they reacted slowly especially at low temperatures. These substances were termed "secondary" acids and bases. The explanation for their behavior appears to be that they are only acids or bases after they have undergone certain electron shifts or other structural transformations requiring activation energy. This concept is useful in explaining why some indicator acids and bases respond rapidly while others are only slowly reversible.

2.2   Water

Water is an amphiprotic solvent with a very high dielectric constant (78.5). The autoprotolysis constant, K_s, for water has the value 10^{-14} at room temperature.

$$K_s = [H_3O^+][OH^-] = 10^{-14}$$

In water the pH scale of 0 to 14 is determined by the 10^{-14} value of K_s.

Water is both a weak acid and a weak base. An acid reacts with the solvent to increase the H_3O^+ concentration, and a base reacts to increase the OH^- concentration. Strong acids dissociate completely in water.

$$\overset{a_1}{} \quad \overset{b_2}{} \quad \overset{a_2}{} \quad \overset{b_1}{}$$

$$HClO_4 + H_2O \rightarrow H_3O^+ + ClO_4^-$$

$$HCl \;\;\; + H_2O \rightarrow H_3O^+ + Cl^-$$

$$HNO_3 + H_2O \rightarrow H_3O^+ + NO_3^-*$$

Although these three "strong" acids actually have different intrinsic acid strengths, they all form the same acid in water (H_3O^+) and thus appear to be of equal acidic strength. The reaction of the acids with water reduces their acidic strength to form the weaker acid, H_3O^+. This is called the *leveling effect*.

Strong bases also react completely with water.

$$\overset{a_1}{} \quad \overset{b_2}{} \quad \overset{a_2}{} \quad \overset{b_1}{}$$

$$(H_2O) + NaOH \rightarrow Na^+ \;\; + OH^-$$

$$(H_2O) + R_4NOH \rightarrow R_4N^+ + OH^-$$

The ions are solvated by water, but water is usually included in the chemical formula for an ion only in the case of a solvated proton. These examples show that OH^- is the strongest base that can exist in water; stronger bases are leveled to the basic strength of hydroxyl ion in aqueous solution.

Weak acids and bases are partially ionized in water. The strength of the acid or base is given by its ionization constant, K_a or K_b. For example,

$$\overset{a_1}{} \quad\quad \overset{b_2}{} \quad \overset{a_2}{} \quad\quad \overset{b_1}{}$$

$$CH_3CO_2H + H_2O \rightleftharpoons H_3O^+ + CH_3CO_2^-$$

$$K_a = \frac{[H_3O^+]\,[CH_3CO_2^-]}{[CH_3CO_2H]} = 1.8 \times 10^{-5}$$

$$\overset{a_1}{} \quad\quad \overset{b_2}{} \quad\quad \overset{a_2}{} \quad\quad \overset{b_1}{}$$

$$H_2O + C_2H_5NH_2 \rightleftharpoons C_2H_5NH_3^+ + OH^-$$

$$K_b = \frac{[C_2H_5NH_3^+]\,[OH^-]}{[C_2H_5NH_2]} = 4.7 \times 10^{-4}$$

---

* In amphiprotic solvents Brönsted has stated that acid–base reactions follow the form,

$$Acid_1 + Base_2 \rightarrow Acid_2 + Base_1$$

where acid$_1$–base$_1$ and acid$_2$–base$_2$ are each conjugate acid–base pairs. Here the products are a weaker acid and base, respectively, than the reactants. Notice that water acts as a weak base in the examples above.

Notice that water is amphoteric; it acts like a base towards an acid and like an acid towards a base.

Salts in water tend to be highly ionized. Salts of a weak acid and a strong base (such as sodium acetate, formed in the titration of acetic acid with sodium hydroxide) or of a weak base and a strong acid (such as ethylammonium chloride, formed in the titration of ethylamine with hydrochloric acid) are usually considered to be completely ionized in water. Therefore, in a typical acid–base titration in water the equilibrium constant, K, for the titration reaction depends only on the dissociation (ionization) constant of the weak acid or base and on the K_s of the solvent.

Example: Titration of a weak acid, HA, with a strong base, NaOH.

$$OH^- + HA \rightarrow A^- + H_2O$$

$$K = \frac{[A^-]}{[OH^-][HA]}$$

Multiplying by $[H^+]/[H^+]$,

$$K = \frac{[A^-][H^+]}{[OH^-][H^+][HA]} = \frac{K_a}{K_s}$$

For an accurate titration K should be large, preferably 10^8 or greater.

Example: Titration of a weak base, B, with a strong acid, HCl.

$$H_3O^+ + B \rightarrow BH^+ + H_2O$$

$$K = \frac{[BH^+]}{[H_3O^+][B]}$$

Multiplying by $[OH^-]/[OH^-]$,

$$K = \frac{[BH^+][OH^-]}{[B][H_3O^+][OH^-]} = \frac{K_b}{K_s}$$

Again K should preferably be equal to 10^8 or greater for an accurate titration.

2.3 Acetonitrile

Aside from rather obvious differences in chemical structure, acetontrile (AN) has at least three different physical constants which distinguish it from water as a solvent. Acetonitrile is a weaker acid and a weaker base than water, the autoprotolysis constant, K_s, is much smaller, and acetonitrile has a lower dielectric constant (36). The work of Kolthoff, Chantooni and Bhomik[2-9] and of Coetzee and Padmanablan[10-11] has contributed greatly to the understanding of acid-base behavior in acetonitrile. This section is a brief summary of some of their findings.

Actonitrile is an amphiprotic solvent which can ionize

$$2CH_3CN \rightleftharpoons CH_3CNH^+ + CH_2CN^-$$

The autoprotolysis constant, K_s, has been reported as $10^{-28 \cdot 6}$.[10] The exact value may be in doubt because strong bases like potassium hydroxide are virtually insoluble in acetonitrile and any attempts to produce significant concentrations of CH_2CN^- by reaction with sodium or potassium metal lead to polymerization of the solvent.[9] Assuming the K_s for AN is $10^{-28.6}$, the pH scale in acetonitrile ranges from 0 to 28.6, with a pH of 14.3 being neutral. This extended pH scale gives a much longer range for potentiometric titrations than water and is advantageous in the resolution of mixtures of acids or bases of different strength.

Acetonitrile is a weaker base and also a weaker acid than water. Thus, "strong" acids are not leveled by acetonitrile but are able to show their differences in acidic strength. Perchloric acid is completely dissociated.

$$HClO_4 + AN \rightarrow H_{AN}^+ + ClO_4^-$$

Hydrochloric acid and other strong acids may be highly ionized in acetonitrile, but the lower dielectric constant of this solvent leads to formation of ion pairs which are incompletely dissociated.

$$HCl + AN \rightleftharpoons H_{AN}^+Cl^- \rightleftharpoons H_{AN}^+ + Cl^-$$

Although each species in an ion pair bears a full positive or negative charge and may have the same color as the free ion, an ion pair conducts essentially no current and behaves chemically more like a molecule in solution. Hence, for calculations of acid-base equilibria the *dissociation constant* is of primary importance. For hydrochloric acid in acetonitrile the dissociation constant is equal to $10^{-8.9}$ and is represented as follows:

$$K_{HCl} = \frac{[H_{AN}^+][Cl^-]}{[HCl]}$$

This is actually an "overall" dissociation constant in which the sum of unionized acid [HCl], and ion pair $[H_{AN}^+Cl^-]$, are included in the denominator. For convenience it is listed simply as [HCl].

15

Dissociation constants have been measured in AN for many acids of the HA type and for conjugate acids of amines and other bases (BH^+ type). Constants for a number of compounds in acetonitrile are listed in Table 2-1; for comparison the pK_a values for the same compounds in water are also given.

TABLE 2.1

Dissociation Constants for Acids and Conjugate Acids of Bases in Acetonitrile*

Acid	pK_{HA}	Base	p$K_{BH^+}(AN)$	p$K_{BH^+}(H_2O)$	ΔpK
Hydrobromic	5.5	Ammonia	16.5	9.2	7.3
Sulfuric	7.25	Methylamine	18.4	10.6	7.8
Hydrochloric	8.9	Dimethylamine	18.7	10.6	8.1
Nitric	8.9	Trimethylamine	17.6	9.8	7.8
2,4,6-Trinitrophenol	11.0	Ethylamine	18.4	10.6	7.8
2,4-Dinitrophenol	16.0	Triethylamine	18.7		
3,5-Dinitrobenzoic	17.2	n-Propylamine	18.2	10.5	7.7
4-Nitrobenzoic	18.7	Pyrrolidine	19.6	11.3	8.3
3-Bromobenzoic	19.5	1,3-Diphenylguanidine	17.9	10.0	7.9
Benzoic	20.7	Pyridine	12.3	5.2	7.1
4-Nitrophenol	20.7	p-Toluidin	11.3	5.1	6.2
4-Hydroxybenzoic	20.8	Aniline	10.7	4.6	6.1
2-Nitrophenol	22.0	Urea	7.7		
Phenol	26.6	Dimethylformamide	6.1	–	–
		Dimethylsulfoxide	5.8	–	–
		Anthraquinone	3.5	–	–

* Data from J. E. Coetzee and G. R. Padmanabian, *J. Phys. Chem.*, 69 (1965), 3193; *J. Am. Chem. Soc.*, 87 (1965), 5005; also, from I. M. Kolthoff, M. K. Chantooni, Jr., and S. Bhomik, *Anal. Chem.*, 39 (1967), 1627.

Measurement of dissociation constants may be done potentiometrically, taking advantage of the fact that the glass electrode measures paH ($-\log a_H$, where a_H is the activity of the solvated proton) reproducibly in acetonitrile. Other useful methods include conductance and spectrophotometric measurements with indicators. In the latter method the pK_{HI} of indicator acids is determined by measuring paH of an acid solution with a glass electrode, and the ratio of the basic to acidic forms of the indicator, $[I^-]/[HI]$, is measured spectrophotometrically.

Log K_{HI} is obtained from the intercept of a plot of

$$\log \frac{[I^-]f_I}{[HI]f_{HI}} \quad \text{vs.} \quad paH$$

$$K_{HI} = \frac{a_H[I^-]f_I}{[HI]f_{HI}}$$

$$\log \frac{[I^-] f_I}{[HI] f_{HI}} = -\log a_H + \log K_{HI}*$$

A partial listing of indicator dissociation constants in acetonitrile is given in Table 2.2. From the indicator constants and from the data in Table 2.1, an indicator may be selected for titration of a given base with

TABLE 2.2

Dissociation Constants for Selected Indicators in Acetonitrile*

Indicator	$pK_{HI}(AN)$	$pK_{HI}(H_2O)$	ΔpK
2-Nitrodiphenylamine	2.0	2.9	4.9
Thymul blue	3.4	—	—
2-Nitro-4-chloroaniline	3.9	−1.0	4.9
2-Nitroaniline	4.9	−0.3	5.2
Neutral red	6.0	∼0.5	5.5
Tropeolin OO	8.0	1.8	6.2
Dimethylaminoazobenzene	10.1	3.3	6.8
Methyl	10.2	4.9	5.3
Bromphenol blue	12.0	—	—
Thymol blue	13.4	—	—
Neutral red	15.6	7.5	8.1
Bromphenol blue	17.5	4.0	13.5
o-Nitrophenol	22.0	7.2	14.8
Phenol red	25.0	7.9	17.1
m-Cresol purple	26.5	8.3	18.2
Thymol blue	27.2	8.9	18.3
Azo violet	30.5	∼ 12	18.5

* Data from I. M. Kolthoff, M. K. Chantooni, Jr., and S. Bhomik, *Anal. Chem.* **39** (1967), 315.

a strong acid (or vice versa) by calculations similar to those used to choose an indicator for an aqueous titration. However, titrations in acetonitrile are complicated by two factors that are not operative in water. One of these is the incomplete dissociation of salts in acetonitrile which stems from the moderately low dielectric constant of this solvent. This effect

* The activity coefficients, f_I and f_{HI}, are evaluated from the limiting Debye–Hückel expression,

$$-\log f = 1.51 Z^2 \sqrt{\mu}$$

(The ionic strength, μ, is always kept small.)

may be illustrated for the titration of a base, B, with a strong acid in acetonitrile.

$$H_{AN}^+ + B \rightarrow BH^+ + AN$$

Neglecting the anion of the titrant acid, the formation constant for this titration is

$$K = \frac{[BH^+]}{[H_{AN}^+][B]} = \frac{1}{K_{BH^+}}$$

If the titrant anion forms an ion pair with BH^+, the dissociation constant of the ion pair must be used to calculate the BH^+ concentration that is substituted into the titration formation constant expression for equilibrium calculations.

$$K_{BHA} = \frac{[BH^+][A^-]}{[BHA]} = \frac{[BH^+]^2}{[BHA]}$$

$$[BH^+] = \sqrt{K_{BHA}[BHA]}$$

Ion pair dissociation constants for NH_4HSO_4 and $LiNO_3$ have been found to be 1.4×10^{-3} and 4.1×10^{-4}, respectively.

Another factor has been observed which complicates acid–base equilibria in acetonitrile. Because of its poor solvating properties and moderately low dielectric constant, the anion of a weak acid is stabilized by association with the free acid.

$$A^- + HA \rightleftharpoons AHA^-$$

The salt of a base may also associate with the free base,

$$BH^+ + B \rightleftharpoons BHB^+$$

but this effect is much less pronounced than the acid anion association just mentioned. These phenomena have been termed "homoconjugation." The formation constants for AHA^- species have been measured in several instances; for example, the formation constant for the AHA^- species of benzoic acid is $10^{3.6}$. As will be shown later (Chap. 3), homoconjugation spreads out the titration curves for acids and makes it more difficult to do a differentiating titration of two acids of different strength. The effect of homoconjugation is minimized by titration in very dilute solution.

Kolthoff, et al.[9] showed that in the absence of significant homoconjugation effects, titration curves in acetonitrile may be calculated in almost the same manner as for titrations in aqueous solutions. An example is shown in Fig. 2.1. The paH at 50% titration is equal to pK_{BH^+} just as in water. The paH after the end point is slightly less acidic than calculated. This has been attributed to formation of an acetonitrile polymer which is somewhat more basic than acetonitrile itself.[9]

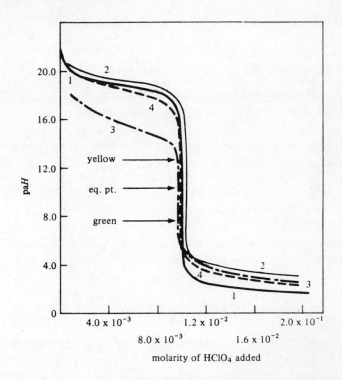

Figure 2.1 *Potentiometric titration of 0.01 M triethylamine in acetonitrile with perchloric acid: (1) calculated curve, (2) curve with HClO$_4$· 1.4H$_2$O (in nitromethane), (3) curve with HClO$_4$ (in anhydrous acetic acid), (4) curve with HClO$_4$ (in nitromethane, 0.84 M in acetic acid). The indicator is p-naphtholbenzein. [Reprinted from I. M. Kolthoff, M. K. Chantooni, Jr., and S. Bhomik, Anal. Chem., 39, (1967): 315. Copyright 1967 by the American Chemical Society. Reprinted by permission of the copyright owner.]*

Mixtures of acids or bases may be assayed by titration in acetonitrile provided the difference in dissociation constants is sufficient. Thus, perchloric acid titration of a mixture of triethylamine (pK_{BH^+} = 18.5) and aniline (pK_{BH^+} = 10.6), where ΔpK_{BH^+} = 7.9, produces a titration curve with excellent end-point breaks for each base. The paH at the first end

19

point is calculated the same way as in aqueous solution.

paH for triethylamine end point $= 1/2(18.5 + 10.6) = 14.6$.

2.4 Acetic Acid

Glacial acetic acid is another amphiprotic solvent with an auto-protolysis constant only slightly different from that of water.

$$2HAc \rightleftharpoons H_{HAc}^+ + Ac^-$$

$$K_s = [H_{HAc}^+][Ac^-] = 10^{-14.45}$$

Acetic acid differs from both water and acetonitrile in that it is much more acidic and has a considerably lower dielectric constant (6.1). The following discussion of acid–base equilibria in acetic acid is based almost entirely on Kolthoff and Bruckenstein's excellent, fundamental studies.[12-14]

In acetic acid strong acids ionize completely (or almost so) but the low dielectric constant causes the positively- and negatively-charged ions to remain primarily as ion pairs, more so than in acetonitrile. The strongest acid in acetic acid is perchloric acid, which has a dissociation constant of only $10^{-4.87}$.

$$K_{HClO_4} = \frac{[H_{HAc}^+][ClO_4^-]}{[HClO_4]} = 10^{-4.87}$$

(In this and in the following instances the equilibrium constant expressions are *overall* dissociation constants. Thus, $[HClO_4]$ represents the analytical concentration of undissociated perchloric acid and includes the concentration of the undissociated ion pair, $H_{HAc}^+ClO_4^-$).

Acetic acid is less basic than water and does not level strong acids. Dissociation constants for several acids are given in Table 2.3. Since titrations of bases are best performed with as strong an acid as possible, the advantage of perchloric acid over the other acids listed is apparent.

The acidic properties of acetic acid solvent are sufficient to cause bases of medium strength to react more or less completely with the solvent.

$$B + HAc \rightleftharpoons BH^+Ac^-$$

The ion pair is only partially dissociated because of the low dielectric constant of acetic acid.

$$BH^+Ac^- \rightleftharpoons BH^+ + Ac^-$$

TABLE 2.3

Overall Dissociation Constants of Acids, Bases, and Salts in Glacial Acetic Acid (−log Autoproyolysis Constant of Glacial Acetic Acid, $pK_s = 14.45$)*

		pK_{HX}
Acids	Perchloric acid	4.87
	Sulfuric acid	7.24
	p-Toluenesulfonic acid	8.46
	Hydrochloric acid	8.55
		pK_B
Bases	Tribenzylamine	5.36
	Diethylaniline	5.78
	Pyridine	6.10
	Potassium acetate	6.10
	Sodium acetate	6.58
	Lithium acetate	6.79
	2,5-Dichloroaniline	9.48
	Urea	10.24
	Water	12.53
		pK_{BHX}
Salts	Sodium perchlorate	5.48
	Diethylaniline perchlorate	5.79
	Tribenzylamine hydrochloride	6.71
	Potassium chloride	6.88
	Urea hydrochloride	6.96
	Lithium chloride	7.08
	Dodecylamine hydrochloride	7.45

* Data from *Treatise on Analytical Chemistry*, part 1, vol. 1, chap. 13.

The overall dissociation constant expression is

$$K_B = \frac{[BH^+][Ac^-]}{[B]}$$

where $[B]$ represents the sum of free base and the undissociated ion pair.

    For bases strong enough to react completely with the solvent, K_B tends to be about the same even though the bases may be of different strength in a less acidic solvent such as water. Dissociation constants for several bases are given in Table 2.3. Acetic acid thus acts as a leveling solvent for aliphatic amines and simple aromatic amines. Aromatic amines with electron-withdrawing substituents such as $-NO_2$ or $-Cl$ are more weakly acidic and are not leveled by acetic acid.

In acetic acid the product of titration of a base, B, with a strong acid is a salt such as $BHClO_4$. Owing to the low dielectric constant, these salts are only slightly dissociated:

$$BHClO_4 \rightarrow BH^+ ClO_4^- \rightleftharpoons BH^+ + ClO_4^-$$

$$K_{BHClO_4} = \frac{[BH^+][ClO_4^-]}{[BHClO_4]}$$

Over-all dissociation constants for various salts are listed in Table 2.3.

Knowing the over-all dissociation constant for one acid and one base, the autoprotolytis constant for glacial acetic acid, K_s, can be calculated. The constant for acetic acid at $25°C$ is 3.6×10^{-15} ($pK = 14.45$).

In the following equations, the equilibria are summarized for the general case where a base is titrated in acetic acid with perchloric acid. The equilibrium constant for each of the steps is indicated in terms of the dissociation constants just described:

$$
\begin{array}{ccccc}
HClO_4 & & B & & \\
\updownarrow K_{HClO_4} & & \updownarrow K_B & & \\
H^+ & + & Ac^- & \xrightleftharpoons{1/K_s} & HAc \\
+ & & + & & \\
ClO_4^- & + & BH^+ & \xrightleftharpoons{1/K_{BHClO_4}} & BH^+ClO_4^-
\end{array}
$$

The over-all reaction then is

$$HClO_4 + B \rightleftharpoons \underset{\text{ion pair}}{BH^+ClO_4^-} + HAc$$

and the equilibrium constant for this reaction is:

$$K = \frac{[BHClO_4]}{[HClO_4][B]} = \frac{K_{HClO_4} K_B}{K_{BHClO_4} K_s}$$

From this, using minor simplifications, the following expression for $[H^+]$ is obtained (unless the base, B, is very weak):

$$[H^+] = \frac{K_s}{K_B[B]} (K_{BHClO_4}[BHClO_4] + K_B[B])^{1/2}$$

This equation can be used to calculate the pH in acetic acid between the start of a titration and the end point.

In many respects the titration of a base with perchloric acid in acetic acid solution is equivalent to titration of a weak base with a weak acid in water. However, in acetic acid the reaction is forced more toward completion by BH^+ and ClO_4^- combining to form ion pairs, $BH^+ClO_4^-$. The formation constant of this ion-pairing in most cases is at least 10^5 which is more than enough to cancel the incomplete ionization of perchloric acid in acetic acid ($K_{HClO_4} = 10^{-4.87}$).

The pH at the start of a titration of a base with perchloric acid in acetic acid can be calculated easily if K_B is known:

$$K_B = \frac{[BH^+][Ac^-]}{[B]}$$

$$[H^+] = \frac{K_s}{(K_B[B])^{1/2}}$$

Thus, the pH of a solution of a pure base in acetic acid changes 0.5 pH unit with a ten-fold change in concentration of the base.

At the end point of a titration of a base with perchloric acid, the pH is that of a pure perchlorate salt in acetic acid. The $[H^+]$ is calculated from the following expression:

$$[H^+] = \left(\frac{K_s K_{HClO_4}}{K_B}\right)^{1/2}$$

Unlike aqueous solution, the pH in acetic acid at the end point is independent of the salt concentration.

The pH of pure perchloric acid in acetic acid is calculated from the dissociation constant of perchloric acid.

$$K_{HClO_4} = \frac{[H^+][ClO_4^-]}{[HClO_4]}$$

$$[H^+] = (K_{HClO_4}[HClO_4])^{1/2}$$

However, after the end point in the titration of a base in acetic acid, the solution contains $BHClO_4$ as well as $HClO_4$. For this situation, the following equation is used to calculate the pH:

$$[H^+] = \frac{K_{HClO_4}[HClO_4]}{(K_{BHClO_4}[BHClO_4])^{1/2}}$$

23

Thus, increasing salt concentration decreases the hydrogen ion concentration, but only by the square root of the salt concentration.

Theoretical titration curves, calculated with the aid of the above equations, are shown in Fig. 2.2.

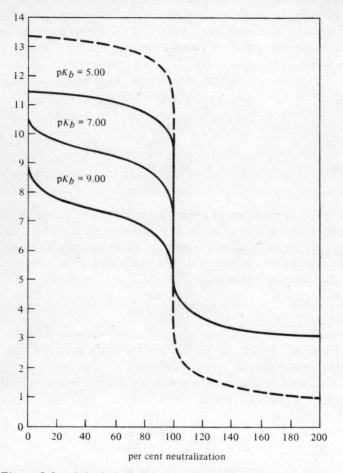

Figure 2.2   *Calculated curves for titration of bases in glacial acetic acid. Dotted lines represent the titration curve of a strong base and strong acid in water. [Reprinted from I. M. Kolthoff,* Treatise on Analytical Chemistry: Part 1, *vol. 1, chap. 13, Fig. 13.4, by permission of the author.]*

The effect of water on titrations carried out in glacial acetic acid is important because water is a weak base. Kolthoff and Bruckenstein[14] give the K_B for water in acetic acid as $10^{-12.33}$ and the equilibrium constant for the following reaction as equal to 34:

$$H_2O + HClO_4 \rightleftharpoons H_3O^+ClO_4^-$$

Water in acetic acid up to 0.5–1.0 M has little effect on the pH of a pure base or on the pH up to the equivalence point in a titration with perchloric acid. At the equivalence point and after, however, water raises the pH and thus shortens the potential break. For example, 0.5 M water in acetic acid raises the final pH ($BHClO_4 + HClO_4$ present) about one pH unit in a typical titration. Larger amounts of water have a more unfavorable effect on the titration.

2.5   Dioxane

     1,4-Dioxane has an even lower dielectric constant (2.2) than acetic acid. Unlike the solvents previously considered, dioxane is not amphiprotic. Dioxane is very weakly basic and reacts with a strong acid such as perchloric acid to form a solvated proton and the acid anion:

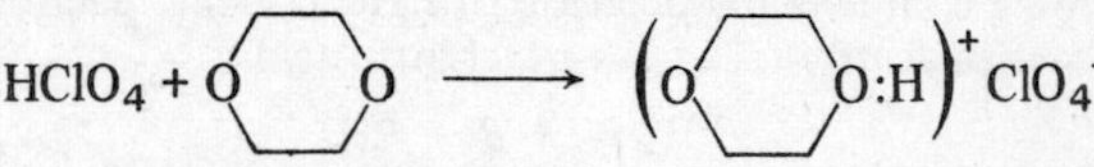

Because of the very low dielectric constant, this ion pair is probably not dissociated to any significant extent.

     A neutral base dissolved in dioxane undoubtedly exists primarily as the free base, B. (Since the base dissolves in dioxane, it is probably solvated, at least weakly.) The reaction of the base with the acid titrant may be viewed as simply the replacement of the weaker base, dioxane, in the ion pair by the stronger base, B:

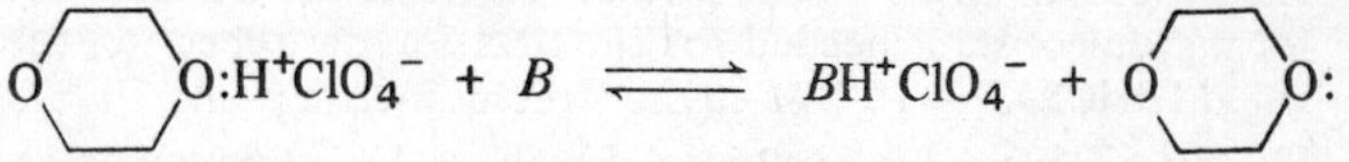

Titration of a base, B, in dioxane may be followed with the aid of a weaker indicator base, I, which changes color when it becomes protonated.

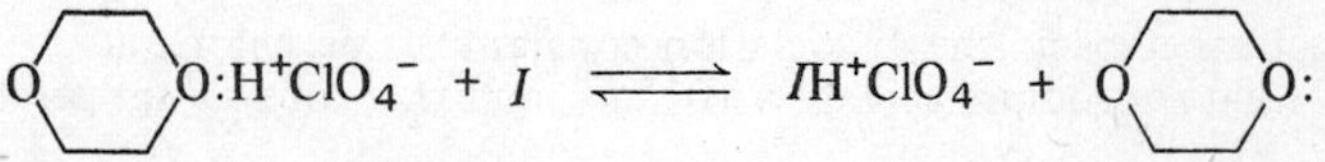

The latter reaction must occur only after all of the stronger base, B, has reacted.

25

PROBLEMS

1. Give a specific example of each of the following:
   (a) autoprotolysis
   (b) lyate ion
   (c) Lewis acid
   (d) leveling effect
   (e) homoconjugation

2. In solvents of lower dielectric constant the tendency to form ion pairs is increased, making it more difficult to maintain an appreciable concentration of an ionic reactant or product in solution. Predict which of the following titration reactions would be more affected by lowering the dielectric constant of the solvent. Explain briefly, and state whether the equilibrium constant for the reaction would be increased or decreased by lowering the dielectric constant.
   (a) $OR^-(\text{titrant}) + BH^+ \rightarrow B + ROH$
   (b) $H_{SH}^+(\text{titrant}) + B \rightarrow BH^+ + SH$

3. Coetzee and Padmanablan found sodium phenoxide to be the strongest base they studied that is soluble and stable in acetonitrile. If pK_a for phenol is 26.6 and pK_s for acetonitrile is 28.6, calculate pK_b for phenoxide in acetonitrile.

4. Assuming complete dissociation of $BHClO_4$, the reaction for titration of a base in acetonitrile with perchloric acid is
   $$H_{AN}^+ + B \rightarrow BH^+$$
   Calculate the minimum formation constant for this titration reaction if conversion of B to BH^+ is to be 99.9% complete at the stoichiometric point when the concentration of BH^+ at the stoichiometric point is
   (a) $10^{-2}\,M$
   (b) $10^{-3}M$

5. Referring to Problem 4, assume now that $K_{BHClO_4} = 10^{-4}$, that at the equivalance point $[BHClO_4] = 10^{-2}M$, and calculate the concentration of BH^+. Taking this into consideration recalculate the minimum formation constant needed for the titration described in Problem 4 when $[BHClO_4] = 10^{-2}M$ at the stoichiometric point.

6. Examine Table 2.1, and predict which of the following bases can be titrated quantitatively (99.9%) at 0.01 M concentration in AN with perchloric acid.
   (a) aniline   (b) urea   (c) sodium 2,4,6-trinitrophenoxide.

7. In acetic acid the dissociation constant for perchloric acid = $10^{-4.87}$, that for sodium acetate = $10^{-6.58}$, and that for sodium perchlorate = $10^{-5.48}$.
   (a) Calculate the equilibrium constant for the following titration in acetic acid: $HClO_4 + NaAc \rightarrow NaClO_4 + HAc$.

(b) Calculate pH$_{HAc}$ of
   (1) A 0.1 M solution of sodium acetate in acetic acid.
   (2) A solution containing 0.036 M sodium acetate and 0.036 M sodium perchlorate.
   (3) A solution containing 0.05 M sodium perchlorate.
   (4) A solution containing 0.03 M perchloric acid and 0.03 M sodium perchlorate.
(c) Using the values calculated, sketch the curve for titration of 0.1 M sodium acetate with 0.1 M perchloric acid.

8. Suggest a method for determining the relative ability of two different bases to react with perchloric acid in dioxane solution.

REFERENCES

1. G. N. Lewis and G. T. Seaborg, *J. Am. Chem. Soc.*, **61** (1939), 1894.
2. I. M. Kolthoff, S. Bruckenstein, and M. D. Chantooni, Jr., *Ibid*, **83**, (1961), 3827.
3. I. M. Kolthoff and M. K. Chantooni, Jr., *Ibid*, **85** (1963), 426.
4. *Ibid.*, **87** (1965), 4428.
5. I. M. Kolthoff, M. K. Chantooni, Jr., and S. Bhomik, *Ibid.*, **88** (1966), 5430.
6. I. M. Kolthoff and M. K. Chantooni, Jr., *J. Phys. Chem.*, **66** (1962), 1675.
7. *Ibid.*, **70** (1966), 856.
8. I. M. Kolthoff, M. K. Chantooni, Jr., and S. Bhomik, *Anal. Chem.*, **39** (1967), 315.
9. *Ibid.*, **39** (1967), 1627.
10. J. F. Coetzee and G. R. Padmanablan, *J. Phys. Chem.*, **69** (1965), 3193.
11. J. F. Coetzee and G. R. Padmanablan, *J. Am. Chem. Soc.*, **87** (1965), 5005.
12. S. Bruckenstein and I. M. Kolthoff, *Ibid.*, **78** (1956), 1; **79** (1957), 1.
13. S. Bruckenstein and I. M. Kolthoff, *Ibid.*, **78** (1956), 10, 2974; **79** (1957), 5915.
14. I. M. Kolthoff and S. Bruckenstein, *Treatise on Analytical Chemistry*, chap. 13, part 1, vol. 1, New York: Interscience, 1959.

CHAPTER 3

Solvents

The general requirements of a solvent for an acid–base titration
are discussed in this chapter. The properties and relative advantages of the
most useful solvents are also explained. Specific solvents and other conditions
for titration of various types of acids and bases are dealt with in later chapters.

3.1   General Requirements

1. *Suitable acid–base properties.* For titration of a weak base the
solvent should also be as weak a base as possible. For titration of an acid
the opposite is true; the solvent should not possess appreciable acidic
properties. This topic is discussed more fully in a later section.

2. *Dissolve a wide variety of solutes readily.* Products of titration
should be soluble, if possible, or at least be crystalline precipitates and not
highly absorptive gels.

3. *Small autoprotolysis constant.* This is needed in order to
provide a long potentiometric range for titrations. This also will be
discussed in Section 3.3.

4. *Fairly high dielectric constant.* Steady potential readings are
obtainable only in solvents of reasonably high dielectric constant. Also,
acid–base reactions are apt to be more favorable and solubility better in
solvents of higher dielectric constant.

5. *High purity.* The solvent should be free of acidic impurities
(for titration of acids) and of basic impurities (for titration of bases). The
acidic blank of a solvent may be determined very easily be adding a drop of
thymol blue indicator solution to 20 ml of the solvent and titrating with
0.1 M tetrabutylammonium hydroxide to a blue color. A reasonably pure

28

solvent should require from 0.01 to 0.02 ml of base (and in no case more than about 0.05 ml) to titrate the acidic impurities. The solvent blank should be subtracted from the volume of base used to titrate samples of acids.

The basic blank of a solvent may be determined by adding a drop of methyl orange solution to 20 ml of the solvent and titrating to a red color with 0.1 M perchloric acid in dioxane. (For acidic solvents such as acetic acid, crystal violet should be used instead of methyl orange). Here also the blank should not exceed 0.05 ml of 0.1 M perchloric acid and preferably should be less.

These simple indicator methods for measuring acidic and basic blanks of a solvent will not always suffice. Sometimes a weakly basic or acidic impurity will act as a buffer and prevent the accurate titration of a sample containing a weak base or acid. In such cases it is necessary to titrate the impurities in the solvent potentiometrically with 0.1 M tetra-butylammonium hydroxide or perchloric acid. Then a blank is subtracted corresponding to the volume of base or acid required to titrate the solvent to the same potential as the equivalence point potential of the base or acid in the sample titration.

Reagent grade solvents often have such a low acidic or basic blank that they may be used without further purification. For other solvents a fairly general method of purification is by simple or fractional distillation, preceeded by one of the following:

(a) Passage through a column of activated alumina.

(b) Passage through a column of molecular sieves, or adding molecular sieves to the solvent container several hours before distillation.

(c) Passage through a column of hydrogen-form cation exchange resin (such as Dowex 50W X8, 100 mesh) to remove basic impurities, or through a column containing a weak-base or strong-base anion exchanger (such as Amberlyst A-26, 100 mesh) to remove acidic impurities.

6. *Unreactive.* The solvent should resist hydrolysis and should not undergo self-condensation induced by strong acid or base. It should not react with solutes to be titrated.

7. *Good solvating ability.* This is needed to avoid homoconjugation effects of the solutes titrated. An example of homoconjugation is the reaction of the anion of a carboxylic acid or phenol to form an association complex with the free acid,

$$A^- + HA \rightleftharpoons AHA^-$$

Homoconjugation may also occur between a base and its salt,

$$BH^+ + B \rightleftharpoons BHB^+$$

but in polar solvents this type of association is usually much weaker than that for the formation of AHA^- complexes. In solvents with good solvating properties, solutes interact with the solvent instead of undergoing self-condensation, and homoconjugation does not occur.

The concentration of a homoconjugation complex increases as the titration proceeds, attaining its maximum concentration when 50% of the acid (or base) has been titrated. The AHA^- complex is a weaker acid than the original acid, HA. This causes the titration curve up to the stoichiometric point (100% titration) to be spread out more than normal on the vertical (millivolt) axis, and there may be an inflection around 50% titration (see Fig. 3.1). Thus, the magnitude of the end-point break is reduced by homoconjugation, and it is more difficult to titrate potentiometrically a mixture of two or more acids of different strength and obtain separate end points for each.

8. *Readily available, inexpensive.*

9. *Not excessively volatile or viscous.*

3.2   Acid–Base Properties

When a base is titrated the following equilibrium is encountered:

$$\underset{\text{(titrant)}}{\underset{\text{acid}_1}{SH_2^+}} + \underset{\text{base}_2}{B} \rightleftharpoons \underset{\text{acid}_2}{BH^+} + \underset{\text{(solvent)}}{\underset{\text{base}_1}{SH}}$$

Here B is the base being titrated, and BH^+ is the titrated form of this base. In order to obtain a sharp end point, this equilibrium must lie far to the right. The most favorable equilibrium will be obtained for any particular base if the solvent has no appreciable basic properties and if the titrant chosen is a very strong acid.

Examination of the chemical equation above shows why this is so. At the stoichiometric point the concentration of solvent greatly exceeds the concentrations of any of the other reactants or products. Therefore, the mass-action concept dictates that a basic solvent will reverse the reaction near the stoichiometric point, and a weak base cannot be titrated with a sharp end point. The strength of the acid titrant that may be used is also limited by the basic properties of the solvent. A weaker titrant will cause the titration equilibrium to be less favorable.

The solvent used for titration of a weak base should not be excessively acidic. A solvent that is very acidic levels most bases to approximately the same strength and makes a differentiating titration of

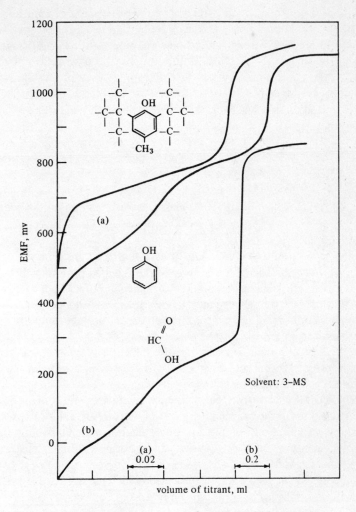

Figure 3.1   *Titration of acids in 3-methylsulfolane with tetrabutylammonium hydroxide. The extra inflection in the titration of phenol (a) and formic acid (b) is caused by homo- conjugation. In the titration of 2,6-di-t-butyl-4-methyl phenol homoconjugation is prevented by steric effects of the bulky groups* ortho *to the phenolic OH. [Reprinted from D. H. Morman and G. A. Harlow,* Anal. Chem., **39** *(1967) 1869. Copyright 1967 by the American Chemical Society. Reprinted by permission of the copyright owner.]*

a mixture of bases impossible. The magnitude of the potentiometric change for titrations is also apt to be more limited in acidic solvents. If the solvent is a fairly strong acid, it may compete with the acid titrant with the result that the titration equilibrium may become unfavorable.

The above considerations concerning acid-base properties of the solvent apply also to the titration of acids, but in reverse. Thus, the solvent used for titration of a weak acid with a strong base should not be excessively basic either.

3.3 Autoprotolysis Constant

At $25°C$ the potential of a glass electrode is given by the equation

$$E = K + 0.059 \text{ pH}$$

where K is a constant that includes the asymmetry potential, and pH = $-\log a_{H_s^+}$, $a_{H_s^+}$ being the activity of the solvated proton in the solvent used. This equilibrium predicts a change in potential of 59 mv (0.059 v) for each unit change in pH. Solvents having a longer pH scale will have a correspondingly longer millivolt range for potentiometric titrations.

The pH scale in any amphiprotic solvent is of course governed by the autoprotolysis constant. Therefore, solvents having a very small auto-protolysis constant ($K_s = 10^{-n}$, where n is large) will be advantageous for acid-base titrations because their longer millivolt scale will provide a better opportunity for differentiating titrations of mixtures of acids or bases of different strength. For example, in t-butyl alcohol, which has a low auto-protolysis constant and a long millivolt range for potentiometric titrations, a mixture of five different acids has been titrated potentiometrically with separate breaks for each acid. Sulfuric acid, which has a K_s of 2.4×10^{-4}, is a very poor solvent for titration of mixtures of bases partly because of its very short millivolt range.

Autoprotolysis constants have been determined for a small but growing number of carefully purified solvents. Practical acid-base titrations are often carried out in solvents containing small amounts of water or other impurities, however, and the potential range actually obtained may be somewhat different from that predicted from the K_s alone. A simple way to measure the practical millivolt range of a solvent is to take the difference in potentials measured (usually with glass and calomel electrodes) after adding a strong acid to the solvent, and again after adding an excess of a strongly basic titrant. Results for a number of solvents are tabulated in Fig. 3.2.

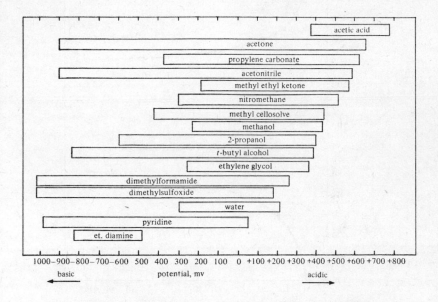

Figure 3.2 *Potential ranges in various solvents measured with glass and calomel electrodes. The calomel electrode is filled with saturated $(CH_3)_4NCl$ in 2-propanol. Acidic solutions contain 1 ml of 0.1 M $HClO_4$ (in dioxane); basic solutions contain 1 ml of 0.1 M $(C_4H_9)_4NOH$ (in 2-propanol).*

The potential range of mixtures of any two miscible solvents can be predicted fairly well from the ranges of the two pure solvents. Fig. 3.3 graphs the acidic and basic potential limits in mixtures of the two solvents, acetone and water. In acidic solutions the addition of increasing proportions of water to acetone causes the potential to decrease rapidly at first and then much more slowly from about 10–15% water to 100% water. Similar effects are observed in the potential at the basic end of the millivolt range. This type of behavior appears to hold for other solvent mixtures where the pure solvents differ appreciably in their acidic or basic potentials, or both. The solvent having the more positive acidic potential (or more negative basic potential) will have its potential brought nearly to that of the second solvent by addition of 10–15% of the latter.

33

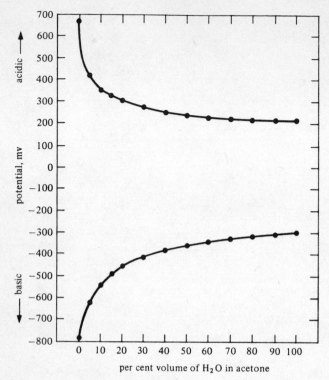

Figure 3.3 *Potential ranges in acetone-water solvent mixtures. Conditions are the same as for Fig. 3.2.*

3.4 Properties of Specific Solvents

For Titration of Either Acids or Bases
1. *Acetone.*

CH_3COCH_3, b.p. 56°, dielectric constant 20.7 (25°C)

The reagent grade solvent has a negligible-to-small acidic and basic blank and may be used without further purification. A large number of phenols, carboxylic acids, and other acidic compounds have been titrated success-fully in acetone.[1] Although no numerical autoprotolysis constant has been reported, the large potential range observed for acid–base titrations suggests that acetone may have a very small autoprotolysis constant, possibly of the order of 10^{-30}.

Bases as weak as aniline (pK_b in H_2O = 9.4) are titrated accurately in acetone with a solution of perchloric acid in dioxane. Primary aliphatic amines such as n-butyl amine must be titrated slowly near the equivalence point because of Schiff's base formation with the solvent.

$$RNH_2 + \begin{array}{c} CH_3 \\ \diagdown \\ CH_3 \end{array}\!\!C=O \rightleftharpoons \begin{array}{c} CH_3 \\ \diagdown \\ CH_3 \end{array}\!\!C=NR + H_2O$$

The equilibrium shifts back to the left as the amine is titrated. Acetone is a good solvent for differentiating titration of mixtures of bases.[2]

2. Acetonitrile.

$$CH_3CN, \text{ b.p. } 80°, \text{ dielectric constant } 36, K_s = 10^{-28.6}$$

Acid-base equilibria in this solvent was discussed in Chap. 2. Acetonitile is an excellent solvent for titration of both acids and bases and for differentiating titration of mixtures of acids and bases.[3] Homoconjugation effects are noted in the titrations of acids and to a lesser extent in the titration of bases. It is necessary to purify acetonitrile to remove both acidic and basic impurities; the purified solvent must be kept dry to avoid further hydrolysis. Acidic impurities may be removed by passing the solvent through a column of an anion exchanger[4,5] and distillation, or by treatment with Linde molecular sieves for 15 minutes before use.[6] Basic impurities are removed by distillation over phosphorous pentoxide, followed by a second distillation over anhydrous potassium carbonate.[7]

3. Alcohols.

Methanol, CH_3OH, b.p. 64.7°, dielectric constant 33, $K_s = 10^{-16.7}$
Ethanol, CH_3CH_2OH, b.p. 78.4°, dielectric constant 24, $K_s = 10^{-19.5}$.
2-Propanol, $CH_3\underset{\underset{OH}{|}}{C}HCH_3$, b.p. 82.4°, dielectric constant 18.3, $K_s = 10^{-20.8}$

2-Propanol has the longest potential range of the three alcohols listed, indicating that its autoprotolysis constant is also the smallest. This, together with its lower volatility, excellent purity (of the reagent grade), lower acidity and adequately high dielectric constant, makes 2-propanol an excellent solvent for titration of a variety of acids and bases. Perchloric acid and quaternary ammonium hydroxide titrants are stable in 2-propanol, permitting the titration of either bases or acids in a homogeneous solvent. Although many types of acids have been titrated successfully in 2-propanol,[8] the weakly acidic properties of the alcohol cause the titration of weak acids to be less sharp than in ketones, acetonitrile, and other less acidic solvents.

Likewise, the basic properties of 2-propanol make the titration of aromatic amines and other weak bases rather poor.

Alcohols have good solvation properties so that homoconjugation effects are not observed for titration of either acids or bases.

4. *Methyl isobutyl ketone.*

$$CH_3COCH_2CH\begin{array}{c}CH_3\\CH_3\end{array}$$ b.p. 117–119°, dielectric constant 13, $K_s = 10^{-28.6}$

Bruss and Wyld[9] found methyl isobutyl ketone (MIBK) to be an excellent solvent for titration of acid mixtures and nitrogen bases. Using glass and calomel electrodes, they found a potential range of approximately 1400 mv in going from excess tetrabutylammonium hydroxide to excess perchloric acid. They titrated successfully a mixture of five different acids potentiometrically, using tetrabutylammonium hydroxide in 2-propanol as the titrant. Bases are titrated with perchloric acid in dioxane.

Commerical MIBK contains small amounts of acidic impurities which may be removed by passage through a column of activated alumina.

5. *Sulfolanes.*

Sulfolane,   b.p. 285°, m.p. 28°, dielectric constant 44

3-Methylsulfolane,   b.p. 276°, m.p. 0°

These solvents are quite similar in their behavior as solvents for acid–base titrations. Sulfolane is cheaper, but 3-methylsulfolane has the advantage of being a liquid at room temperature. Both are good solvents for dissolving most samples. If desired, a mixture of the two may be used, or sulfolane may be warmed slightly before use. After the sample and first increments of titrant (in 2-propanol, or dioxane) have been added, freezing of sulfolane is no longer a problem.

Sulfolanes have the longest potential range yet reported of any solvent used for acid–base titrations. Morman and Harlow[10] report a potential difference of approximately 1750 mv in going from a solution containing excess tetrabutylammonium hydroxide to one containing excess perchloric acid. Bases are titrated in sulfolane with perchloric acid in dioxane or with specially prepared perchloric acid in sulfolane, which is stable for as long as one year.[11] Acids are titrated with tetrabutyl-ammonium hydroxide in 2-propanol.

The long potential range of sulfolanes is ideal for differentiating titrations of mixtures of either acids or bases. However, the poor solvating properties of sulfolanes cause many acids and even some bases to undergo homoconjugation. This makes the titration curves more drawn out (with regard to potential) but does not prevent effective titration of acid or base mixtures.

Sulfolanes may be purified by fractional distillation under vacuum, or more conveniently by passage through a column of freshly activated alumina.

6. *Mixed solvents.*

(a) *Organic-water mixtures.* Sometimes it is necessary to titrate a weak acid or base in a sample that is in aqueous solution. By adding a water-miscible organic solvent, the sharpness of the titration end point may often be improved. For example, addition of nine volumes of acetone to each volume of aqueous sample solution gives a sharper titration of a weak acid or base than would be obtainable in water alone (although not as good as would be obtained in 100% acetone). The acidic and basic potential limits for aqueous-organic solvent mixtures may be estimated approximately from the data in Fig. 3.2, as illustrated in Fig. 3.3. A longer potential range for a solvent mixture generally results in a better titration of a weak acid or base.

(b) *ASTM titration solvent.* This consists of 50% toluene, 49.5% 2-propanol, and 0.5% water.[12] It dissolves a wide variety of petroleum and other industrial samples and permits the titration of many acids (with potassium hydroxide in 2-propanol) and bases (with hydrochloric acid in 2-propanol). However, acids as weak as phenol are not titratable, and weaker bases such as pyridine (pK_b in H_2O = 8.9) give poor results.

(c) *Glycol-hydrocarbon.* The G-H solvents introduced by Palit[13] consist of equal volumes of a glycol (ethylene or propylene glycol) and a "hydrocarbon" such as 2-propanol or chloroform. Glycols have good solvating power for many solutes and dissolve salts of carboxylic acids and dicarboxylic acids especially well. Addition of 2-propanol (or chloroform for high molecular weight compounds) reduces the viscosity and increases the sharpness with which salts and other bases may be titrated. Bases are titrated with perchloric or hydrochloric acid in the same G-H solvent; acids are titrated with G-H solutions of sodium hydroxide. Weaker acids and bases such as phenol (pK_a in H_2O = 9.8) and aniline

37

(pK_b in H_2O = 9.4) do not give very sharp end points when titrated in G-H solvents.

For Titration of Acids
1. t-*Butyl Alcohol.*

$$CH_3-\underset{\underset{CH_3}{|}}{\overset{\overset{CH_3}{|}}{C}}-OH \qquad \text{b.p. } 82°, \text{ dielectric constant } 10.9$$

t-Butyl alcohol is less acidic than the lower primary and secondary alcohols, probably because of the inductive effect of the three methyl groups on the carbon atom to which the hydroxyl group is attached. Thus, acids as weak as phenol (pK_a in H_2O = 9.8) can be titrated in *t*-butyl alcohol with good results. The solvating ability of *t*-butyl alcohol is good enough to prevent homoconjugation during the titration of acids. This is a distinct advantage over most other solvents used for titration of acid mixtures, in which homoconjugation of carboxylic acids and phenols causes the potential readings to be drawn out so that the various end-point breaks are less pronounced.

The long potential range (see Fig. 3.2) indicates that *t*-butyl alcohol must have a very small autoprotolysis constant. This is also suggested by the considerable difference in dissociation constants of acids (see Table 3.1) and by the fact that benzoic acid, which is only a moderately weak acid, has such a small dissociation constant.

TABLE 3.1

Dissociation Constants of Some
Acids in *t*-Butyl Alcohol[14]

Acid	pK_{HA}
Perchloric	4.0
2,4-Dinitrophenol	10.5
Benzoic	14.9

Acids in *t*-butyl alcohol are generally titrated with a quaternary ammonium hydroxide dissolved in another solvent, such as 2-propanol. During a titration stable protentials are obtained in *t*-butyl alcohol containing excess base. This is in contrast to solvents such as acetone and pyridine in which unsteady basic potentials are often obtained.[15] Sulfuric and other strong acids may be quantitatively titrated in *t*-butyl alcohol.

Reagent grade *t*-butyl alcohol has a very low acidic blank and usually requires no further purification. Ordinary distillation further reduces the blank.

2. *Dimethylformamide (DMF)*.

$HCON(CH_3)_2$, b.p. 153°, dielectric constant 27.0, $K_s = 10^{-18.0}(20°C)$

According to Tezé and Schaal[16] the autoprotolysis constant of DMF is approximately 10^{-18}, and the basic form in the presence of a hydroxide titrant is probably

$$HO\overset{\overset{\displaystyle O^-}{|}}{C}HN(CH_3)_2$$

DMF dissolves most organic solutes unusually well, including many salts. Titration curves have normal shape in the buffer region, indicating an absence of homoconjugation effects. Thus, dimethylformamide is well suited for titration of acid mixtures. Many types of individual acids have been titrated quantitatively in DMF.[17-19]

Dimethylformamide hydrolyzes partially to form formic acid, especially when the solvent is wet. The acid impurity is removed by passage through a strong-base anion exchange column. Reagent grade DMF has a reasonably low acidic blank. Further purification is achieved by distillation under reduced pressure, preferably with a nitrogen · atmosphere.

3. *Dimethylsulfoxide (DMSO)*.

$$CH_3\overset{\overset{\displaystyle O}{|}}{S}CH_3,$$ b.p. 100° (decomp.), dielectric constant 46.7, $K_s = 10^{-33}$

Dimethylsulfoxide is an excellent solvent and ought to be advantageous for titration of acids. Kolthoff and Reddy[20] studied acid–base behavior in DMSO and reported an autoprotolysis constant of $10^{-17.3}$, a value that has been disputed by later workers. These authors found that OH^- from quaternary ammonium hydroxide titrants apparently reacts to form the lyate ion, which attacks the solvent causing it to turn dark and form weakly basic products. For this reason DMSO cannot be recommended for titration of most weak acids with quaternary ammonium hydroxide titrants. However, Barnes and Mann[21] obtained good results for titration of various amine salts as acids in DMSO.

Courtot-Coupez and Le Démézer[22] found the autoprotolysis constant of DMSO to be 10^{-33}, and they reported acid dissociation constants for many different acids. These authors used the sodium salt of dimethyl sulfoxide ($Na^+CH_3SOCH_2^-$) to neutralize the acids studied. This is an extremely strong base, but it is unstable and is easily decomposed by oxygen (in air), moisture, or quaternary ammonium salts. However, Price and Whiting[23] successfully titrated phenols, alcohols, and other very weak acids with sodium DMSO in a dry nitrogen atmosphere using a visual indicator.

4. Ethylenediamine.

$H_2NCH_2CH_2NH_2$, b.p. $117°$, dielectric constant 12.5, $K_s = 10^{-15.3}$

Anhydrous ethylenediamine is a powerful solvent for dissolution of a wide variety of acids. Titration of very weak acids is possible in ethylenediamine using sodium aminoethoxide titrant.[24] Because of its pronounced basic properties, ethylenediamine is a leveling solvent for most acids and is generally unsuitable for differentiating titration of acid mixtures. Also, ethylenediamine is highly corrosive and requires careful handling to avoid contamination by carbon dioxide.

Schaap, *et al.*[25] and also Mukherjee, Bruckenstein, and Badawi[26] have studied acid–base behavior in anhydrous ethylenediamine. They have reported dissociation constants for a number of acids and salts in ethylenediamine.

5. Pyridine.

b. p. $115.5°$, dielectric constant 12.3

Pyridine has been used successfully by Cundiff and Markunas[27] and others as a solvent for titration of many acids and acid mixtures with quaternary ammonium hydroxide titrants. It is a weakly basic, stable solvent with a sufficiently high dielectric constant to permit stable potentiometric readings. Although pyridine is apparently aprotic, a large potential range is obtainable for titrations with a quaternary ammonium hydroxide dissolved in an alcohol (see Fig. 3.2). Strong acids are leveled by pyridine, but mixtures of medium to weak acids can be resolved if there is a sufficient difference in strength of the various acids. Differentiating titrations of phenols and carboxylic acids in pyridine are hindered somewhat by homoconjugation effects.

Fritz and Marple[15] obtained high results for titration of weakly acidic alkyl phenols in pyridine, especially when the titration was performed rather slowly. This was attributed to partial decomposition of the tetrabutylammonium hydroxide titrant in the pyridine system. This error was not encountered in the titration of stronger acids.

The acid blank of commerical pyridine may be reduced to a small value by shaking it with activated alumina for 5 minutes and filtering it through a glass fiber filter containing a layer of diatomaceous earth.[28] Reagent grade pyridine generally has only a small blank. Further purification may be achieved by distillation over barium oxide.

For Titration of Bases
1. *Acetic acid.*

$$CH_3CO_2H, \text{ b.p. } 118.5°, \text{ dielectric constant } 6.1, K_s = 10^{-14.45}$$

Acid-base behavior in acetic acid was discussed in Chap. 2. Acetic acid is very widely used as the solvent for titration of weak bases. It dissolves most bases readily, and visual or potentiometric end points are usually sharp. The reagent grade material is very pure and has almost no basic blank. Perchloric acid titrants prepared in acetic acid are stable for long periods of time.

Acetic acid is a leveling solvent for most bases. Except for mixtures of very weak bases, differentiating titrations of bases should be done in a less acidic solvent such as acetonitrile or acetone.

2. *Acetic anhydride.*

$$(CH_3CO)_2O, \text{ b.p. } 140°, \text{ dielectric constant } 20.7, K_s = 10^{-14.5} (20°C)$$

Fritz and Fulda[29] showed that addition of 5–20% by volume of acetic anhydride to acetic acid, nitromethane, or acetonitrile results in much sharper titration curves for caffeine and other very weak bases. Addition of acetic anhydride extends the acidic end of the potential range by 100 mv or more. This enhancement of acidity was attributed to removal of the last traces of water, which is basic and weakens the acidity of the solvated proton. Pietrzyk[30] suggested that the primary enhancement of acidity is through the formation of a new, more acidic species, $(CH_3CO)_2OH^+$ and CH_3CO^+.

$$CH_3CO_2H_2^+ + (CH_3CO)_2O \rightleftharpoons (CH_3CO)_2OH^+ + CH_3CO_2H$$
$$(CH_3CO)_2OH^+ \rightleftharpoons CH_3CO^+ + CH_3CO_2H$$

In a comprehensive paper Streuli[21] found that pure acetic anhydride is also advantageous for titration of amides, tert. amines, salts, and certain other weak bases. Primary and secondary amines are not titratable (except as the amide in some cases) because they are acetylated by the solvent during the titration.

41

Titrations in acetic anhydride may be followed potentiometrically using glass and calomel electrodes, or with visual indicators.[29] The tirant must be made up in acetic acid or dioxane because perchloric acid is not stable for very long in acetic anhydride.[30] Reagent grade acetic anhydride may be used without further purification.

3. *1,4-Dioxane.*

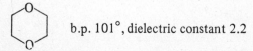 b.p. 101°, dielectric constant 2.2

Acid–base behavior in dioxane was discussed in Chap. 2. Although the high electrical resistance of solutes dissolved in dioxane makes potentiometric titrations impossible using ordinary titrimeters, acid–base titrations may be performed very nicely using visual indicators. For example, aliphatic amines and nitrogen heterocyclic bases give excellent results when titrated with perchloric acid in dioxane using a modified methyl orange or methyl red indicator.[32]

Chloroform, carbon tetrachloride, chlorobenzene, and other aprotic solvents are similar to dioxane in their applicability for titration of bases using visual indicators. (These solvents, however, do not readily dissolve perchloric acid, so another titrant or solvent must be used.) For example, Safarik has made extensive use of chloroform for titration of alkaloids using dimethyl-yellow indicator and p-toluenesulfonic acid in chloroform as the titrant.[33,34]

4. *Formic acid.*

HCO_2H, b.p. 100.7°, dielectric constant 56.1 (25°C), $K_s = 10^{-6.7}$

Anhydrous formic acid is rather unstable and is very hygroscopic. Wehman and Popov[35] considered it imperative to use freshly distilled formic acid. Also, the potential range in formic acid is short, owing to the rather large autoprotolysis constant.

Despite these shortcomings, formic acid does have some favorable properties. Popov and Marshall[36] titrated caffeine and other very weak bases in anhydrous formic acid with p-toluenesulfonic acid using a modified quinhydrone electrode. In formic acid, caffeine has a pK_b of 0.55, and the very weak base urea has a pK_b of 1.75. Formic acid is a powerful solvent for materials that ordinarily are dissolved with difficulty. Tetracene[37] and basic groups in polymers have been determined by dissolution in anhydrous formic acid, then adding 7 times as much acetic acid and titrating with perchloric acid.

5. *Nitromethane.*

CH_3NO_2, b.p. $100.8°$, dielectric constant 35.9 $(30°C)$

Nitroalkanes are known to enolize to form a weakly acidic *aci* form that can be neutralized with base.

$$CH_3NO_2 \rightleftharpoons CH_2=\overset{+}{N}\overset{\diagup O^-}{\underset{\diagdown OH}{}}$$

Based on conductance studies, isolation of neutralization products from acid–base reactions, and other evidence, Paul, *et al.* [38] have proposed autoionization of nitromethane as follows:

$$2CH_3NO_2 \rightleftharpoons CH_3NO_2H^+ + CH_2NO_2^-$$

No autoprotolysis constant has been measured, although the long potential range (see Fig. 3.2) suggests a very small autoprotolysis constant.

The high dielectric constant and weakly acidic properties make nitromethane advantageous as a medium for titration of bases. Nitromethane dissolves most organic bases well but is a poor solvent for most salts. Streuli[39] titrated many bases potentiometrically in nitromethane with 0.05 M perchloric acid dissolved in the same solvent. A plot of half-neutralization potential in nitromethane against pK_b in water gave a straight line with a slope of 78 mv/pK unit. No leveling effects were noted for bases even as strong as piperidine (pK_b in water = 2.9). The potentiometric titration curves were normal except for titration of urea and unsubstituted amides, which gave curves with unusually steep slopes. This behavior was attributed to intermolecular hydrogen bonding of the amides.

6. *Sulfuric acid.*

H_2SO_4, b.p. $340°$(d), dielectric constant 84, $K_s = 2.4 \times 10^{-4}$

Anhydrous sulfuric acid has several properties that make it a potentially useful solvent for titration of bases. It is an excellent solvent for most organic compounds; because of the unusually high dielectric constant, many substances ionize extensively in sulfuric acid. Its lack of basic properties recommend it as a solvent for titration of extremely weak bases.

Thus far, the disadvantages of sulfuric acid have discouraged its use as a solvent for practical acid–base titrations. The major disadvantages are the instability of many compounds in sulfuric acid, the high autoprotolysis constant which severely limits the magnitude of any end-point break, and the strongly acidic properties which level most bases and make it difficult to find a sufficiently acidic titrant.

Leyden, Smith, and Underwood[40] have successfully determined benzophenone, aliphatic ketones, benzaldehyde, heptaldehyde, benzamide, and benzoic acid *as bases* by conductometric titration in sulfuric acid. As titrant they employed tetra(hydrogen-sulfato)boric acid, $HB(HSO_4)_4$. (Leyden, *et al.* found sulfur trioxide too reactive.) The conductometric end point may not coincide exactly with the equivalence point, but results are satisfactory if the titrant is standardized in the same way that a basic sample is titrated.

PROBLEMS

1. What is homoconjugation? Explain how it affects an acid–base titration curve. How may homoconjugation be minimized?

2. Dichloroacetic acid is a liquid at room temperature and is a stronger acid than acetic acid. List any advantages dichloroacetic acid might have as a solvent for titration of bases. List any possible disadvantages.

3. Explain why the autoprotolysis constant is an important factor in choosing a solvent for an acid–base titration. Suggest a simple experimental way to estimate the autoprotolysis constant of an amphiprotic solvent.

4. A solvent of "four-nines" purity (99.99%) is usually considered quite good. Calculate the milliliters of $0.1\ M$ tetrabutylammonium hydroxide needed to titrate the acidic impurity in 25 ml of a solvent of specific gravity 0.90 if the solvent contains 0.01% by weight of an acid having an equivalent weight of 100. Is this solvent sufficiently pure for practical acid–base titrations?

5. What effect does a small percentage of water (5% for example) have on the titration of a weak base or weak acid in another solvent? Explain why water is especially to be avoided in the titration of a weak acid in dimethylformamide.

6. Methyl Cellosolve is an excellent solvent for dissolution of solid organic and inorganic compounds, but it gives a shorter and less sharp end-point breaks than some other solvents. Suggest a solvent that might be added to a sample dissolved in methyl Cellosolve to improve the end point in each of the following titrations: (a) a weak acid, (b) a weak base.

7. Propylene carbonate (the cyclic ester of 1,2-propylenediol and carbonic acid) has a high dielectric constant. Examine Fig. 3.2 and decide whether propylene carbonate might be a good solvent for titration of weak acids or weak bases. What other information would you need to evaluate it more completely as a practical solvent for acid–base titrations?

8. List one suitable solvent for each of the following acid–base titrations:
   (a) Titration of a very weak tertiary amine.
   (b) Titration of a mixture of an aliphatic amine (a medium strength base) and an aromatic amine (a weak base).
   (c) Titration of a mixture of p-nitrophenol (a moderately weak acid) and phenol (a weak acid).
   (d) Titration of a mixture of acetic acid and sodium acetate in which sodium acetate is first titrated as a base and then the total acetic acid is titrated in the same solvent with a basic titrant.

REFERENCES

1. J. S. Fritz and S. S. Yamamura, *Anal. Chem.*, **29** (1957), 1079.
2. J. S. Fritz and C. A. Burgett, *Anal. Chem.* **44** (1972), 1673.
3. J. S. Fritz, *Anal. Chem.*, **25** (1953), 407.
4. H. B. Van Der Heijde, *Anal. Chim. Acta*, **17** (1957), 512.
5. J. S. Fritz and W. Glover, Unpublished work, 1970.
6. E. J. Forman and D. N. Hume, *Talanta*, **11** (1964), 129.
7. P. Walden and E. J. Birr, *Z. Physik Chem.* (Leipzig), **A114** (1929), 269.
8. G. A. Harlow, C. M. Noble, and G. E. A. Wyld, *Anal. Chem.*, **28** (1956), 787.
9. D. B. Bruss and G. E. A. Wyld, *Anal. Chem.*, **29** (1957), 232.
10. D. H. Morman and G. A. Harlow, *Anal. Chem.*, **39** (1967), 1869.
11. J. F. Coetzee and R. J. Bertozzi, *Anal. Chem.*, **41** (1969), 860.
12. L. Lykken, P. Porter, H. D. Ruliffson, and F. D. Tuemmler, *Indust. Eng. Chem., Anal. Ed.*, **16** (1944), 219.
13. S. R. Palit, *Ind. Eng. Chem., Anal. Ed.*, **18** (1946), 246.
14. L. W. Marple and G. J. Scheppers, *Anal. Chem.*, **38** (1966), 553.
15. J. S. Fritz and L. W. Marple, *Anal. Chem.*, **34** (1962), 921.
16. M. Tezé and R. Schaal, *Bull. Chem. Soc. France*, **29** (1962), 1372.
17. J. S. Fritz, *Anal. Chem.*, **24** (1952), 306, 674.
18. J. S. Fritz and R. T. Keen, *Anal. Chem.*, **24** (1952), 308.
19. I. M. Kolthoff, M. K. Chantooni, and H. Smagowski, *Anal. Chem.*, **42** (1970), 1622.
20. I. M. Kolthoff and T. B. Reddy, *Inorg. Chem.*, **1** (1962), 189.
21. K. K. Barnes and C. K. Mann, *Anal. Chem.*, **36** (1964), 2502.
22. J. Courtot-Coupez and M. Le Démézet, *Bull. Chem. Soc. France*, **36** (1969), 1033.
23. G. C. Price and M. C. Whiting, *Chem. & Ind.* (1963), 775.
24. M. L. Moss, J. H. Elliott, and R. T. Hall, *Anal. Chem.*, **20** (1948), 784.
25. W. B. Schaap, R. E. Bayer, J. R. Siefker, J. Y. Kim, P. W. Brewster, and F. C. Schmidt, *Record Chem. Prog.*, **22** (1961) 197.

26. L. M. Mukherjee, S. Bruckenstein, and F. A. K. Badawi, *J. Phys. Chem.*, **69** (1965), 2537.

27. R. H. Cundiff and P. C. Markunas, *Anal. Chem.*, **28** (1956), 792.

28. W. M. Banick, *Anal. Chem.*, **34** (1962), 296.

29. J. S. Fritz and M. O. Fulda, *Anal. Chem.*, **25** (1953), 1837.

30. D. J. Pietrzyk, *Anal. Chem.*, **39** (1967), 1367.

31. C. A. Streuli, *Anal. Chem.*, **30** (1958), 997.

32. J. S. Fritz, *Anal. Chem.*, **22** (1950), 578.

33. L. Safarik, *Cesk. Farm.*, **11** (1962), 387.

34. J. Kucharsky and L. Safarik, *Titrations in Nonaqueous Solvents*, Amsterdam: Elsevier Pub. Co., 1965, p. 156.

35. T. C. Wehman and A. I. Popov, *J. Phys. Chem.*, **72** (1968), 4031.

36. A. I. Popov and J. C. Marshall, *J. Inorg. & Nuclear Chem.*, **19** (1961), 340, *Ibid*, **24** (1962), 1662.

37. J. S. Hetman, *Chem. & Ind.* London, 1964, 232.

38. R. C. Paul, R. Kaushal, and S. S. Pahil, *J. Indian Chem. Soc.*, **44** (1967), 920, 964, 995; *Ibid*, **46** (1969), 26.

39. C. A. Streuli, *Anal. Chem.*, **31** (1959), 1652.

40. D. E. Leyden, D. L. Smith, and A. L. Underwood, *Anal. Chem.*, **35** (1963), 307.

CHAPTER 4

Titrants

4.1 Acidic Titrants

Perchloric Acid

As stated earlier (Chap. 1, p. 3) perchloric acid is the preferred titrant for titrations carried out in acetic acid and other nonbasic solvents because it is the strongest of the common mineral acids (see Table 2.3). In water and other solvents having significant basic properties the leveling effect (p. 3) is such that other strong acids will serve as well as perchloric acid. In acetic acid, however, perchloric acid gives a longer potentiometric break than hydrochloric acid and a much longer break than nitric acid.

Perchloric acid titrant is made up in various solvents depending on the titration to be carried out. Perchloric acid in acetic acid is commonly used for titration of weak bases in acetic acid, nitromethane, chloroform, and many other solvents. The titrant is prepared simply by dissolving the required amount of 70-72% perchloric acid (which is approximately $HClO_4 \cdot 2H_2O$) in acetic acid. Usually a 0.01-0.5 M titrant is used. If a very weak base is to be titrated, the water introduced with the perchloric acid is removed by adding a calculated amount of acetic anhydride to combine with the water. The acid–catalyzed reaction of acetic anhydride with water is fairly rapid. When titrating a primary or secondary amine that might react with acetic anhydride, it is important to avoid any excess acetic anhydride in the titrant. Properly prepared titrants are stable for long periods of time.

Sometimes it is desirable to exclude acetic acid from a titration system because of its leveling effect on mixtures of certain bases. In such cases, perchloric acid in 1,4-dioxane is a good titrant. The brown color which sometimes develops in these solutions (but causes no titration

47

errors) can be avoided by using reagent grade dioxane or by first purifying the dioxane by shaking with cation-exchange resin. As with acetic acid, titrants are prepared simply by adding the calculated amount of 70–72% perchloric acid to dioxane. The small amount of water introduced has a negligible effect on the titration of most bases. Solutions of perchloric acid in dioxane are stable and may be used for titration of bases in almost any solvent.

Perchloric acid in sulfolane has been recommended for titration of bases in nonaqueous solvents.[1] Coetzee and Bertozzi prepared an anhydrous titrant by titrating anhydrous hydrogen chloride with silver perchlorate in sulfolane.

$$AgClO_4 + HCl \rightarrow AgCl(s) + HClO_4$$

The titrants thus prepared were found to be stable for one year without change in titer or hydrogen ion activity. Perchloric acid appears to be completely dissociated in sulfolane.

Perchloric acid dissolved in an alcohol such as 2-propanol is satisfactory for titration of bases that are strong enough to give sharp end points in alcoholic solvents. Perchloric acid appears to be more stable than hydrochloric acid, which reacts slowly with an alcohol to form the alkyl halide. However, alcoholic solutions of perchloric acid should *never be heated* because under anhydrous conditions violently explosive perchlorate esters may be formed. (By contrast solutions of perchloric acid in acetic acid can safely be heated or even distilled.[2])

Sulfonic Acids

p-Toluenesulfonic acid (dissolved in chloroform) and several other sulfonic acid titrants have been used successfully for titration of bases. Pietrzyk and Belisle[3] studied twelve substituted aromatic sulfonic acids for use as titrants in methyl isobutyl ketone and acetic acid. These sulfonic acids are weaker acids than perchloric acid and in general give shorter potentiometric end-point breaks. 2,4-Dinitrobenzenesulfonic acid (used as the dihydrate) is approximately equal to perchloric acid in acidic strength. Aromatic sulfonic acids have the advantage of being soluble in more organic solvents than perchloric acid.

For titrations in solvent mixtures containing a considerable proportion of acetic anhydride, Pietrzyk[4] recommends a solution of 2,4,6-trinitrobenzenesulfonic acid (TNBS) as a titrant. This acid is significantly stronger than 2,4-dinitrobenzenesulfonic acid and is virtually the equal of perchloric acid. TNBS gives good results for titration of primary amides in 90% acetic anhydride-10% acetic acid, while titration with a perchloric acid titrant under the same conditions leads to low results because of partial acetylation.

Trifluoromethanesulfonic acid, CF_3SO_3H, in glacial acetic acid has been proposed as a titrant.[5,6] In acetic acid, it is as strong an acid as perchloric; and no precipitate is formed during titration of potassium acid phthalate or other bases. However, trifluoromethanesulfonic acid is quite expensive and appears to offer no major advantages over perchloric acid.

Lewis Acids

A number of workers have investigated the use of Lewis acids for titration of various bases. For example, pyridine and quinoline have been titrated conductometrically with boron tribromide in nitrobenzene.[7] Tertiary aromatic amines may be titrated quantitatively in acetyl chloride with $SnCl_4$ or $TiCl_4$ using either crystal violet or benzanthrone as a visual indicator.[8] Hitchcock and Elving[9] obtained reasonably good accuracy for titration of nitrogen bases in acetonitrile and oxygen bases (alcohols, for example) in benzene with tin(IV) chloride. They obtained AB_2 type adducts for titration of some oxygen bases.

In preparing titrants, Lewis acids should be handled in a dry box, and the titrant solutions must also be protected from moisture to prevent hydrolysis. The only advantage of Lewis acid titrants appears to be in the titration of very weak bases, such as alcohols. However, the greater bulk of Lewis acids (compared to solvated H^+) might make it possible to titrate an ordinary base in the presence of a sterically hindered base.

Miscellaneous Titrants

Anhydrous hydrogen bromide dissolved in acetic acid may be used to titrate epoxides.[10]

$$HBr + R\text{--}CH\text{--}CH_2 \longrightarrow RCHCH_2Br$$
$$\underset{O}{\diagdown\diagup} \qquad\qquad \underset{OH}{|}$$

Since hydrogen bromide is quite a strong acid, nitrogen bases may be titrated as well.

Paul, et al.[11] showed that sulfur trioxide, dissolved in acetic acid or acetyl chloride, may be used for titration of pyridine and other tertiary amines.

Standardization of Acidic Titrants

Potassium acid phthalate (KHP),

equivalent weight 204.2, is a well established primary standard acid for basic titrants in aqueous solution. In glacial acetic acid, KHP serves as a primary standard *base* for standardization of perchloric acid titrants.

$$HClO_4 \;+\; \underset{\text{}}{\text{(o-C}_6\text{H}_4)(CO_2K)(CO_2H)} \longrightarrow \underset{\text{}}{\text{(o-C}_6\text{H}_4)(CO_2H)(CO_2H)} \;+\; KClO_4$$

KHP is sparingly soluble in acetic acid, and heat must be used to dissolve it completely. Experimental details of the standardizing titration are given in Chap. 8, Procedure 1.

Tris(hydroxymethyl)aminomethane (THAM), $(CH_2OH)_3CNH_2$, equivalent weight 121.1, is also an excellent primary standard.[12] THAM is soluble in most solvents and may be used for standardization of almost any strongly acidic titrant. Solvents containing excess acetic anhydride should not be used in conjunction with THAM since the amine function in THAM may be acetylated.

$$\overset{\displaystyle NH}{\underset{\displaystyle \parallel}{}}$$

Diphenylguanidine, $C_6H_5NHCNHC_6H_5$, equivalent weight 211.3, has the advantage of being soluble in many aprotic solvents. For use as a primary standard, diphenylguanidine should be purified by triple recrystallization from toluene and then dried at around $100°C$.

4.2   Basic Titrants

Alkali Metal Bases

Alcoholic potassium hydroxide is a satisfactory titrant for moderately weak acids. Various sodium and potassium alcoholates may also be used. However, a solution of sodium or potassium methoxide in benzene-methanol is a better titrant for weak acids as well as for the titration of acidic compounds in general. The methoxide titrant is prepared by reacting the alkali metal with methanol and then diluting it with benzene so that the benzene-methanol ratio is 9 or 10 to 1. Benzene serves as an inert diluent for the titrant and reduces the amount of methanol added during the titration. This is important because if much methanol is present, the acidic nature of methanol reduces the sharpness with which weak acids can be titrated in a non-aqueous solvent.

$$
\begin{array}{cccc}
\text{base} & \text{acid} & \text{base} & \text{acid} \\
OMe^- \;+\; & HA & \rightarrow \quad A^- \;+\; & MeOH \\
\text{(titrant)} & & &
\end{array}
$$

In the titration of most weak acids, results are improved markedly by titrating with methoxide in benzene-methanol instead of methoxide in methanol alone.

Quaternary Ammonium Hydroxides

Tetrabutylammonium hydroxide in 2-propanol or benzene-methanol is probably the most widely used titrant for titration of acids in nonaqueous solution. This and other quaternary ammonium hydroxides have at least two major advantages over other titrants. In almost every case the tetraalkylammonium salt of the titrated acid is soluble in the solvents commonly used. Sodium or potassium salts of titrated acids frequently form gelatinous precipitates. The other advantage of tetraalkylammonium hydroxides is that excellent potentiometric curves are obtained using ordinary glass and calomel electrodes. The "alkali error" limits the use of the glass electrode in conjunction with alkali-metal titrants, particularly in basic solvents. Harlow, Noble and Wyld[13] prepared quaternary ammonium hydroxide titrants in 2-propanol by passing a solution of the quaternary ammonium iodide through a large anion exchange column in the hydroxyl form:

$$R_4N^+I^- + Anex - OH^- - R_4N^+OH^- + Anex - I^-$$
(in 2-PrOH)   (in 2-PrOH)

They found it necessary to use a very slow flow rate to obtain good conversion of the iodide to the hydroxide. A modification of their method (Chap. 8, Procedure 9) uses a macroreticular anion exchange resin which gives faster exchange rates in nonaqueous solution than the older gel type resin. The titrant prepared by Procedure 9 is of good quality and is free from carbonate and amine impurities (see below). It is perfectly stable for 2–4 weeks at room temperature and for longer periods when kept in a refrigerator.

Cundiff and Markunas[14] recommended a different method for the preparation of tetrabutylammonium hydroxide in benzenemethanol. Tetrabutylammonium iodide or bromide is dissolved in methanol and shaken with silver oxide:

$$Bu_4N^+X^- + Ag_2O + MeOH \rightarrow Bu_4N^+OH^- + Bu_4N^+OMe^- + 2AgX(s)$$

After filtration the solution is diluted with benzene so that the final titrant is about 10 parts benzene to 1 of methanol. Cluett[15] demonstrated that the titrant prepared in this manner is approximately an equal molar mixture of hydroxide and methoxide. He neutralized the hydroxide by reacting it with excess glacial acetic acid and measured the water formed by a Karl Fisher titration. The methoxide content was determined by subtracting the hydroxide content from the total basicity.

It is difficult to prepare tetrabutylammonium hydroxide and other quaternary titrants that do not contain some weaker base as an impurity. Any strongly basic titrant must of course be carefully prepared and handled to avoid contamination by carbonate. However, tetraalkylammonium hydroxides are subject to decomposition via the Hofmann elimination.

$$(R_3NCH_2CH_2-)\,{}^+OH^- \rightarrow R_3N + {}^-CH_2CH_2OH$$
$$(R_3NCH_2CH_2-)\,{}^+OH^- \rightarrow R_3N + CH_2{=}CH_- + H_2O$$

The second reaction is faster and usually predominates. The tertiary amine formed is a weaker base than the quaternary ammonium hydroxide, and in the titration of an acid it may cause an error similar to that in an aqueous acid–base titration with sodium hydroxide that is not carbonate-free. It is, in fact, difficult to prepare quaternary ammonium hydroxide titrants that are completely free from carbonate impurities. The effect of weak base impurities on the titration of tetrabutylammonium hydroxide with a strong acid is shown in Fig. 4.1. The extra inflection in curve A and the lower inflection in curve B are due to carbonate impurity; the additional inflection in curve B is the result of tertiary amine from partial decomposition of the titrant.

Preparation of tetrabutylammonium hydroxide by silver oxide reaction in an ice bath results in a titrant that contains only small quantities of impurities. Further purification may be accomplished by the method of Marple and Fritz.[16] (See Chap. 8, Procedure 9c, p. 135.) The quaternary ammonium hydroxide is filtered through activated charcoal to remove any silver oxide or silver complexes; then water is added and the solution is extracted with benzene to remove any tertiary amine that might be present. Next the aqueous solution is passed through an anion exchange column in the hydroxyl form to free the solution from carbonate. Finally, most of the water is distilled off under reduced pressure (approximately, 20 torr) until a crystalline hydrate of tetrabutylammonium hydroxide is formed. This hydrate may be kept in the refrigerator for extended periods of time without decomposition. When titrant is needed the hydrate may be dissolved in 2-propanol, or a titrant with less water may be prepared by distilling water from the hydrate until a vapor pressure from 7 to 10 torr is obtained, then diluting the base (which is approximately $2\,M$) to the desired concentration with 20% 2-propanol-80% benzene.

Water is to be avoided in basic titrants because it is weakly acidic and reduces the sharpness and magnitude of the end-point break when acid samples are titrated. Marple[16] showed that in t-butyl alcohol solutions of tetrabutylammonium hydroxide, methanol is almost as acidic as water and that ethylene glycol is even more acidic. Moreover, addition of up to 8% (by volume) of 2-propanol caused very little change in the potential of a basic solution. For this reason, 2-propanol is a suitable diluent for quaternary ammonium hydroxide titrants.

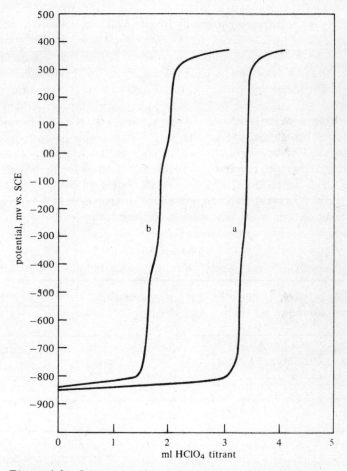

Figure 4.1 *Impurities in tetrabutylammonium hydroxide solutions: (a) solution known to contain some carbonate, (b) same solution after slight decomposition showing an additional inflection due to tertiary amine impurity.* [*Reprinted from L. W. Marple and J. S. Fritz,* Anal. Chem., **34** *(1962): 797. Copyright 1962 by the American Chemical Society. |Reprinted by permission of the copyright owner.|*

The stability of quaternary ammonium hydroxide titrants that are properly protected from carbon dioxide depends on (1) the nature of the titrant solvent, and (2) the structure of the quaternary ammonium hydroxide. Quaternary ammonium hydroxides are relatively stable in alcohols, but are unstable in basic solvents such as pyridine.[17] Harlow[18] found that a small proportion of water ($\sim$1%) greatly increases the stability of tetraalkylammonium hydroxides in 2-propanol. Dilution of a 2-propanol solution of tetraethylammonium hydroxide with an inert solvent such as benzene or toluene, however, decreases the stability of the titrant solution.

In the Hofmann elimination reaction of quaternary ammonium bases the hydrogen atoms on the beta carbons are the most susceptible to attack. Thus, the ethyl group with three hydrogens on the beta carbon is especially vulnerable. Harlow[18] found phenyltrimethylammonium hydroxide to be the least stable titrant studied, with tetraethylammonium hydroxide being the next least stable. (All titrants were made up in 2-propanol.) Tetrabutylammonium hydroxide and methyltributylammonium hydroxide are much more stable. Tetramethylammonium hydroxide, which has no beta carbon atom, is by far the most stable. In 2-propanol, it has a half-life of 26 days at 50°C, compared to 7.1 days for tetrabutylammonium hydroxide. Stabilities of selected titrants are listed in Table 4.1.

TABLE 4.1

Stabilities of Quaternary Ammonium Hydroxide Titrants in 2-Propanol.[18]

Quaternary ammonium titrant	H_2O content wt. %	Half-life, days	
		35°C	50°C
Tetramethyl-	0.09	–	26
Methyltributyl-	–	400	–
Tetrahexyl-	0.09	127	6.1
Tetrabutyl-	0.10	123	7.1
Tetrapropyl-	0.10	–	2.5
Tetraethyl-	0.10	3	0.2

Quaternary ammonium titrants are most stable at lower temperatures. For example, tetraethylammonium hydroxide in 2-propanol is approximately 16,000 times more stable at −15°C than at 25°C.[18]

Because of its excellent stability, tetramethylammonium hydroxide ought to be a useful titrant. Pritchett[19] prepared tetramethylammonium hydroxide by passing a 0.1 M solution of potassium methoxide in benzene-methanol through a cation-exchange column in the tetramethylammonium form. This titrant is very pure and is more stable in storage than other tetraalkylammonium titrants. A disadvantage of the tetramethylammonium titrant is that the tetramethylammonium salt of the acid titrated precipitates during the titration in many cases.

Very Strong Bases

Much stronger bases than tetraalkylammonium hydroxides or alkali metal alkoxides have been used as titrants. Higuchi, Concha, and Kuramoto[20] used a solution of a lithium aluminum amide to titrate alcohols and other extremely weak acids. Kellum and Uglum[21] applied the method to titration of weakly acidic silanols.

$$LiAlH_4 + 4R_2NH \rightarrow (R_2N)_4LiAl + 4H_2$$

$$(R_2N)_4LiAl + 4ROH \rightarrow ROLi + (RO)_3Al$$

Corwin and Ellingson[22] used a solution of sodium triphenyl-methane in 1 to 1 ethyl ether-toluene to titrate pyrroles as acids. The end point can be detected by observing the red color of the first excess of the highly-colored titrant. Unfortunately this titrant is extremely reactive; and water, carbon dioxide, oxygen, and solvent impurities must be rigorously excluded.

Price and Whiting[23] used the sodium salt of dimethyl sulfoxide, $Na^+(CH_2SOCH_3)^-$ (sometimes called "dimsylsodium"), for the quantitative titration of very weak acids such as water, phenols, alcohols, nitromethane, amides, thiols, diphenylamine, pyrrole, phenylacetylene, cyclopentadiene, and indene. The base is prepared in a dry, inert atmosphere following implicitly the directions of Corey and Chayakovski.[24] Titrations are performed in a closed container flushed with nitrogen, and all reagents are introduced by means of a syringe. A 1-M solution of dimsylsodium in DMSO is added from an "anaerobic" buret. The end point of a titration is indicated by a small amount of added triphenylmethane, which turns red when the first permanent excess of base is added.

$$Na^+(CH_2SOCH_3)^- + (C_6H_5)_3CH \rightarrow Na^+(C_6H_5)_3C^- + CH_3SOCH_3$$

Standardization of Basic Titrants

Usually, basic titrants are standardized against benzoic acid, which is an excellent primary standard. The standardizing titration is probably best done under conditions similar to those that will be used for titration of acid samples. Any blank stemming from acidic impurities in the solvent must be measured and taken into account in calculating the molarity of the titrant.

PROBLEMS

1. When is it advantageous to use acetic anhydride for removing small amounts of water from perchloric acid titrant prepared in glacial acetic acid? Why should excess acetic anhydride in the titrant be avoided?

2. One liter of 0.10 M perchloric acid in acetic acid is to be prepared. (a) Calculate the required volume of 72% perchloric acid, specific gravity 1.68. (b) If the acetic acid contains 0.3% water (by volume) calculate the weight of acetic anhydride needed to react with the water in the perchloric acid and acetic acid.

3. A mixture of a medium-strength base and a weak base is to be titrated in acetone. Perchloric acid and other strong acid titrants made up in acetone are unstable on storage. Suggest a suitable solvent for the acid titrant. Why is perchloric acid in acetic acid unsuitable for this particular titration?

4. Why does sodium methoxide in benzene-methanol give sharper titration end points than those obtained using a titrant made up in methanol alone? Explain how sodium 2-propoxide in 2-propanol might compare with sodium methoxide in methanol as a titrant for weak acids.

5. What advantages does tetrabutylammonium hydroxide have over sodium methoxide as a titrant? What disadvantages?

6. How could you determine whether a quaternary ammonium titrant contains any tertiary amine? Which R groups result in a structure in which a quaternary ammonium hydroxide would resist decomposition to a tertiary amine? Which groups are more susceptible to decomposition?

7. A solution of a quaternary ammonium hydroxide titrant is stored in the refrigerator to minimize decomposition. What error might result if the cold titrant is used in a quantitative titration?

8. For what type of acid sample is it advantageous to use a very strongly basic titrant such as sodium dimethylsulfoxide in DMSO? What precautions must be observed when using this titrant?

REFERENCES

1. J. F. Coetzee and R. J. Bertozzi, *Anal. Chem.*, **41** (1969), 860.
2. G. F. Smith (private communication).
3. D. J. Pietrzyk and J. Belisle, *Anal. Chem.*, **38** (1966), 969.
4. D. J. Pietrzyk, *Anal. Chem.*, **39** (1967), 1367.
5. E. S. Lane, *Talanta*, **8** (1961), 849.
6. R. C. Paul, S. K. Vasisht, K. C. Malhotra, and S. S. Pahil, *Anal. Chem.*, **34** (1962), 820.

REFERENCES

7. M. C. Henry, J. F. Hazel, and W. M. McNabb, *Anal. Chim. Acta*, **15** (1956), 187.
8. J. Singh, R. C. Paul, and S. S. Sandhu, *J. Chem. Soc.*, **81** (1959), 845.
9. E. T. Hitchcock and P. J. Elving, *Anal. Chim. Acta*, **27** (1962), 501; *Ibid.*, **28** (1963), 301.
10. A. J. Durbetaki, *Anal. Chem.*, **28** (1956), 2000.
11. R. C. Paul, S. P. Natula, P. Mayer, and S. K. Gondal, *J. Sci. Research*, **21** (1962), 533, 552.
12. T. R. Williams and J. D. Hartley, *Chemist-Analyst*, **50** (1961), 114.
13. G. A. Harlow, C. M. Noble, and G. E. A. Wyld, *Anal. Chem.*, **28** (1956), 787.
14. R. H. Cundiff and P. C. Markunas, *Anal. Chem.*, **28** (1956), 792.
15. M. L. Cluett, *Anal. Chem.*, **31** (1959), 610.
16. L. W. Marple and J. S. Fritz, *Anal. Chem.*, **34** (1962), 796.
17. H. B. van der Heijde and E. A. M. F. Dahmen, *Anal. Chim. Acta*, **16** (1957), 378.
18. G. A. Harlow, *Anal. Chem.*, **34** (1962), 1487.
19. J. Pritchett, "Stability of Organic Bases and Solvents; Determination of Organic Acids in Tertiary Butyl Alcohol" (M. S. Thesis, Iowa State Univ., 1960).
20. T. Higuchi, J. Concha, and R. Kuramoto, *Anal. Chem.*, **24** (1952), 685.
21. G. E. Kellum and K. L. Uglum, *Anal. Chem.*, **39** (1967), 1623.
22. A. H. Corwin and R. C. Ellingson, *J. Am. Chem. Soc.*, **64** (1942), 2098.
23. G. C. Price and M. C. Whiting, *Chem. & Ind.* (1963), 115.
24. E. J. Corey and M. Chayakovski, *J. Am. Chem. Soc.*, **84** (1962), 866.

CHAPTER 5

End-point Detection

5.1 Potentiometric Titrations

Usually potentiometric titration is the method chosen for mixtures, for quite weak acids or bases, and for samples containing an acid or base of unknown strength. Once a given type of sample has been titrated potentiometrically, a visual indicator can conveniently handle the titration of subsequent samples of the same general type. Or, derivative methods or other rapid potentiometric techniques that indicate the equivalence point without plotting an entire potentiometric curve may be used.

5.2 Equipment

Potentiometric titrations in most nonaqueous solvents can be performed very easily with a pH meter or other direct-reading titrimeter that will permit use of a glass electrode, which has a very high resistance. If a pH meter is used, the millivolt scale and not the pH scale should generally be used. Some titrimeters are commercially available that provide for delivery of titrant at a fixed rate and automatic recording of the entire potentiometric titration curve.

Potentiometric titrations are satisfactory in most organic solvents except those of very low dielectric constant such as benzene, chloroform, dioxane, and other ethers. Potentiometric titrations in chloroform or dioxane can be carried out by placing the electrodes very close together[1] to minimize the effect of IR drop. Some acids have been successfully titrated in benzene, toluene, or gasoline using a vibrating reed electrometer.

Malmstadt and Fett[2] have developed an automatic titrator that locates the end point of a titration by electronically taking the second derivative of the potentiometric curve. This double differentiation of the potentiometric curve enables the end point to be detected without knowing the actual potential at the equivalence point. The instrument switches itself off when the end point is reached. Since this instrument does not have a high input resistance, the glass electrode cannot be used for titrations. However, several satisfactory low-resistance electrode combinations (see Section 5.3) can be used for practical titrations in nonaqeuous solutions.[3]

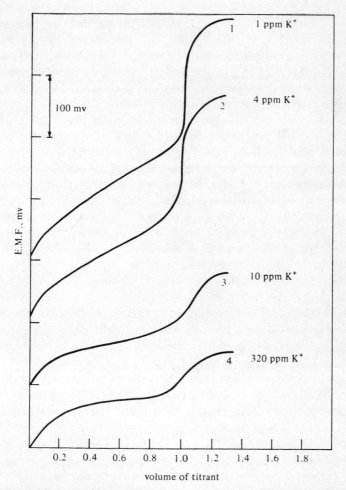

Figure 5.1   *Titration of phenol in presence of potassium ion. [Reprinted from G. A. Harlow,* Anal. Chem., **34** *(1962): 148. Copyright 1962 by the American Chemical Society. Reprinted by permission of the copyright owner.]*

5.3   Indicator Electrodes and Indicating Electrode Pairs

The glass electrode is by far the most widely used indicator electrode. A general-purpose glass electrode is satisfactory for titration of both acids and bases in a wide variety of solvents. In most cases, steady potential readings are quickly attained.

The author prefers to keep a glass electrode in water when not in use to avoid possible dehydration of the outer layers of the glass membrane. For precisely reproducible potentials, some workers prefer to store the electrode in the organic solvent being used. However, in some cases, this may cause the electrode to be very slow in coming to equilibrium.

The glass electrode is not a satisfactory indicator electrode when used in some basic solvents. A glass electrode has actually been used as a reference electrode for titrations in butylamine with sodium methoxide. It is believed that the glass electrode is subject to a large "alkali error" when used in basic solvents in conjunction with sodium alkoxide titrant. The potassium ion also causes trouble (Fig. 5.1), but the very large tetra-butylammonium ion is apparently free from this difficulty.

Various metal electrodes have been used successfully for titrations in nonaqueous solvents. Zeidler[4] proposed a gold indicator electrode, and Jander and Klaus[5] used a special gold–gold electrode pair for titrations of bases in acetic acid. In the latter the gold reference is placed in a capillary. A film of insoluble gold acetate forms on the surface, and the authors suggested that the gold electrode follows the acetate ion concentration of the solution rather than the hydrogen ion concentration.

Harlow, Nobel and Wyld[6] found that either an anodically or a cathodically polarized platinum electrode will serve as an indicator electrode for titration of acids in ethylenediamine. Apparently the surface of the electrode is charged with either oxygen or hydrogen, depending on whether the platinum is treated anodically or cathodically. Both hydrogen and oxygen electrodes are known to respond to changes in pH. The anodized platinum produces curves having the greatest potential range and the sharpest inflections. However, to obtain reproducible potentials the electrode has to be anodized before each titration and has to stand in the solvent for 2 or 3 min. before starting the titration.

Shain and Svoboda[7] used two platinum indicator electrodes, polarized by a constant 1 μa current, for titration of acids in acetone with tetrabutylammonium hydroxide. The difference in potential of the electrodes reaches a maximum at the equivalence point. The shape of the titration curve varies with the polarizing current (Fig. 5.2).

Malmstadt and Vassallo[3] examined a number of electrode systems for use with automatic, derivative titrations of acids in acetone. Platinum (10% rhodium), nickel, chromel, copper, and rhodium all respond as indicator electrodes. Graphite (pencil lead) is a satisfactory reference electrode. A platinum (10% rhodium)–graphite electrode combination was recommended. While the absolute potential differences are not

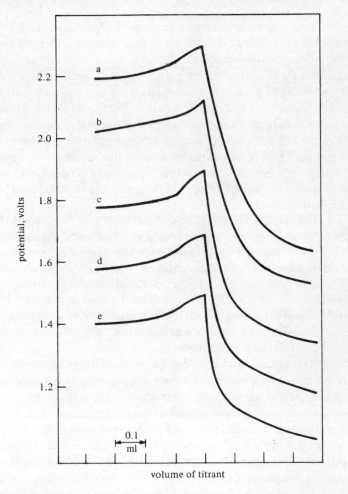

Figure 5.2 *Effect of variation of polarizing current on titration curves of acetic acid. Polarizing current in μa: (a) 10, (b) 5, (c) 2, (d) 1, (e) 0.5. [Reprinted from H. V. Malmstadt and D. A. Vassallo,* Anal. Chem., **31** *(1959): 862. Copyright 1959 by the American Chemical Society. Reprinted by permission of the copyright owner.]*

necessarily reproducible, the electrode materials do respond rapidly and provide sharp changes of potential at the equivalence point.

5.4   Reference Electrodes

Several types of calomel reference electrodes are available commercially. The fiber-type calomel is quite common. This can be used in most nonaqueous solvents if the dielectric constant is greater than about 5. However, the fiber can become plugged up rather easily, causing erratic potential readings. A sleeve-type calomel electrode provides a good interface between the electrode and the test solution, but it may permit excessive flow of electrolyte solution from the calomel electrode into the solution being titrated. A porous plug (ceramic junction) calomel electrode, which has a small cylinder of porous material in the tip, appears to be a good compromise between the first two types mentioned. The cylinder provides good contact, but the flow of electrolyte from the calomel electrode should be slight.

For titrations of acids Cundiff and Markunas[8] observed that sharper and longer potentiometric breaks are obtained if the aqueous electrolyte in a conventional calomel electrode is replaced by a saturated methanolic solution of potassium chloride. While many workers have confirmed the practical utility of this modified calomel electrode for non-aqueous titration of acids, Marple and Fritz[9] observed that titration curves are frequently displaced on the potential scale by as much as 50 mv. This was attributed to a variable junction potential between the solution and the modified calomel electrode.

Reproducible potentials can be obtained using a glass electrode in conjunction with a colomel reference electrode that has a suitable salt bridge. The part of the salt bridge that contacts the solution being titrated should contain a nonaqueous solvent so that the potential range will not be diminished by the acidic (or basic) properties of water. Preferably the salt bridge should not contain potassium salts which can also reduce the potential range of acids.[10] The salts used should be selected so that the conductance of the salt bridge will not be blocked by formation of an insoluble precipitate at an aqueous–organic solvent interface. Several salt bridges have been devised that fulfill these stipulations. For example, the assembly shown in Fig. 5.3 gives potentials for titration of acids in t-butyl alcohol that do not vary more than 1 or 2 mv over a period of at least one month. Unfortunately this salt bridge is somewhat cumbersome.

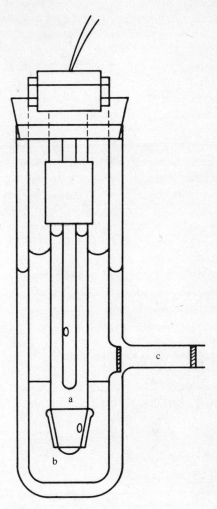

Figure 5.3 *Reference electrode for use in* t-*butyl alcohol: (a) saturated potassium chloride in water; (b) aqueous phase, 2-phase mixture* H_2O–t-*butyl alcohol*–KCl; *(c)* t-*butyl alcohol saturated with tetrabutylammonium bromide. [Reprinted from L. W. Marple and J. S. Fritz,* Anal. Chem., **34** *(1962): 796. Copyright 1962 by the American Chemical Society. Reprinted by permission of the copyright owner.]*

A simple arrangement is to replace the aqueous potassium chloride in a calomel electrode (preferably a porous plug type) with a saturated solution of tetramethylammonium chloride in 2-propanol.[11] This electrode gives stable and apparently reproducible potential readings in conjunction with a glass indicator electrode for titration of acids in solvents such as t-butyl alcohol, 2-propanol, and dimethylformamide.

A silver–silver chloride reference electrode also performs well if a suitable salt bridge is used. Kolthoff and Reddy[12] used a silver–silver chloride with a salt bridge containing dimethylsulfoxide saturated with sodium chloride for a reference electrode in DMSO. Tezé and Schaal[13] found that a reference electrode of DMF saturated with calomel in conjunction with a salt bridge of DMF saturated with potassium chloride performed well over a period of several months. A silver wire coated with silver chloride dipping into a saturated solution of tetramethylammonium chloride in 2-propanol, contained in the outer shell from a porous plug calomel electrode, also works well for titration of acids in various non-aqueous solvents.[11]

A simple calomel reference electrode containing aqueous potassium chloride works satisfactorily for titration of bases in acetic acid and other solvents. A calomel or silver–silver chloride electrode with an appropriate nonaqueous salt bridge may also be used, but in most cases the advantage over the ordinary calomel electrode appears to be slight. For titrations in acetic anhydride a calomel electrode with a salt bridge containing potassium chloride, lithium chloride, or lithium perchlorate in acetic anhydride has been used.[14] Streuli used a silver–silver chloride electrode in acetic saturated anhydride with silver chloride and lithium chloride.[15]

5.5 Indicators

For Titration of Bases

Crystal violet or the closely related compound methyl violet is the most widely used visual indicator for the titration of weak bases. These two indicators give a vivid and quickly reversible color change for titrations carried out in a wide variety of solvents. With increasing acidity, crystal violet changes from violet (its basic form) to green and finally to yellow. Frequently, blue, blue-green and yellow-green shades are also observed near the end point of a titration because of the mixing of the various forms of the indicator. The ionization of crystal violet in media of increasing acidity is shown below:

$$\left(Me_2N-\bigotimes\right)_3 \cdot COH$$

$$H^+ \big\Updownarrow$$

violet: $\left(Me_2N-\bigotimes\right) C^+ \longleftrightarrow$

$$Me_2\overset{+}{N}=\bigotimes=C -\left(\bigotimes NMe_2\right)_2 \longleftrightarrow etc.$$

$$\big\Updownarrow$$

green: $Me_2\overset{+}{\underset{H}{N}}-\bigotimes-\overset{+}{C} -\left(\bigotimes-NMe_2\right)_2 \longleftrightarrow etc.$

$$\big\Updownarrow$$

yellow: $\left(Me_2\overset{+}{\underset{H}{N}}-\bigotimes\right)_2 \overset{+}{C}-\bigotimes-NMe_2 \longleftrightarrow etc.$

Most bases can be titrated successfully if the first complete disappearance of a violet tinge is taken as the end point. However, it is advisable first to titrate each type of compound potentiometrically in order to select the correct indicator or end-point color.

Higuchi, Feldman, and Rehm[16] suggested that the behavior of acid–base indicators in glacial acetic acid is best represented by the general reaction,

$$SHA + IHAc \rightarrow IHA + SHAc$$

where S is the solvent or some other protophilic base present; I is the indicator; HA is a strong acid; and HAc represents acetic acid. By spectrophotometric methods using various buffers, they measured the equilibrium constants for a number of indicators and were able to establish the following order (decreasing basicity) of indicators in acetic acid:

Ethyl red, pinacyanol, 4-dimethylamino-4'-nitrosostilbene,

65

quinaldine red, *m*-nitro-N,N-dimethylanilide, brilliant
cresyl blue, 1-naphtholbenzein, nile blue A, sudan III,
sudan IV.

Quinaldine red and those below it are suitable for titration of bases in
glacial acetic acid. Nile blue A and sudan III can be used for the titration
of very weak bases such as urea.

Kolling and his associates[17,18] studied the transition ranges of
several additional indicators in acetic acid.

Methyl red may be used for titration of bases in 1,4-dioxane,
glycol-2-propanol mixtures, and in several other solvents provided acetic
acid is not present.

For Titration of Acids

In solvents such as DMF, acetone, and pyridine it has been observed
empirically that thymol blue gives good results for titration of medium
strength acids, azo violet for weak acids, and *p*-nitro-*p*-aminoazobenzene
for titration of very weak acids. A more precise method is to measure the
transition ranges of many indicators and to select an indicator with a
transition range that includes the potential at the stoichiometric point as
determined by a potentiometric titration. This has been done for several
indicators in acetone,[3] although the transition ranges were not determined very precisely.

For meaningful transition ranges of indicators in nonaqueous
solvents, potentiometric titration curves and other potentiometric
measurements must be reproducible. This is possible only if the proper
electrode system is used. With the development of a modified calomel
reference electrode,[9] in conjunction with a glass electrode, excellent
reproduction of potentials is possible.

Fritz and Gainer[19] have measured the transition ranges of
several indicators in pyridine by both visual and by spectrophotometric
methods. (See Fig. 5.4.) The solution was buffered by partial titration of
various acid mixtures with tetrabutylammonium hydroxide. The transition
ranges of the indicators were observed visually as buffer acids were titrated
with base. For spectrophotometric measurements, the spectra of the full
acidic and full basic forms of each indicator were measured. Then, using an
appropriate wavelength setting, the buffer acids were titrated with
tetrabutylammonium hydroxide and the milliliters of titrant was noted
at the point of the first detectable increase in absorbance and at the point
of no further increase in absorbance. An exact duplicate solution was titrated
potentiometrically, and the emf in millivolts was noted at the milliliters of

titrant corresponding to the acidic and basic ends of the previously observed indicator transitions. Many replicate titrations showed that with each buffer the potentials corresponding to various milliliters of titrant base could be reproduced within a few millivolts.

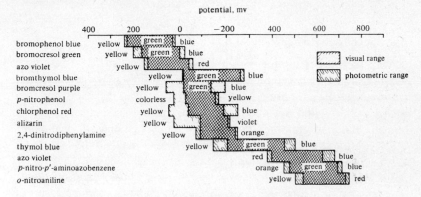

Figure 5.4 *Indicator transition ranges in pyridine solvent. [Reprinted from J. S. Fritz and F. E. Gainer,* Talanta, **13** *(1966): 939.*

A similar procedure has been employed to determine transition ranges of indicators in *t*-butyl alcohol.[20] Fig. 5.5 shows the transition ranges of the indicators and the colors at each end of the range. In the

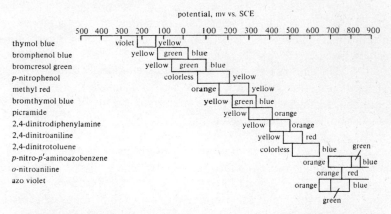

Figure 5.5 *Indicator transition ranges in t-butyl alcohol solvent. [Reprinted from L. W. Marple and J. S. Fritz,* Anal. Chem., **35** *(1963): 1305. Copyright 1963 by the American Chemical Society. Reprinted by permission of the copyright owner.]*

case of sulfonephthaleins, a definite green color forms at an intermediate point in the conversion from the yellow form to the basic blue form. The basic edge of the transition range of o-nitroaniline could not be located with certainty. Both o-nitroaniline and p-nitro-p-aminoazobenzene function well as indicators for the titration of very weak acids.

5.6   Spectrophotometric Titrations

A spectrophotometer may be used to follow an acid–base titration and to locate the equivalence point(s). Two possibilities present themselves. One is to use the absorption spectra of the substances titrated or the titrant; the other is to follow the absorbance of an added visual indicator.

Bases and mixtures of bases may be titrated in acetic acid with 0.5 M perchloric acid in acetic acid.[21,22] Use of made of the fact that aromatic amines absorb light in the ultraviolet region, and that the absorption maxima of the free base and protonated base are at different wavelengths. Aromatic amines are titrated on the long wavelength side of the peak where the basic form absorbs. A plot of absorbance against milliliters of titrant gives a

shape curve. Pyridine, quinoline, and their analogs are titrated at a wavelength where the protonated form of the base absorbs, giving a titration curve with a

shape. Bases having a pK_b (in water) less than 10 cannot be titrated directly in acetic acid by this method because they are completely protonated by the solvent. Thus, it is seen that this method is best for very weak bases. However, stronger bases can be titrated in acetonitrile.

The photometric titration method seems ideally suited to the differentiating titration of mixtures of aromatic amines. In Fig. 5.6 the photometric curve for titration of a mixture of 2-methyl-5-nitro-aniline and 4-methyl-2-nitroaniline is shown. The absorbance is measured at 522 nm, in which the basic form of 4-methyl-2-nitroaniline is the only absorbing species. The potentiometric titration curve for this same mixture shows only a faint indication of the individual end points for the compounds titrated.

The titration of acidic substances may also be followed spectrophotometrically. McKinney and Reynolds[23] were able to titrate phenols in butylamine with 0.05 M sodium hydroxide in absolute ethanol. A wavelength was chosen for each titration in which the phenolate ion absorbed but the free phenol did not. In every case studied the phenolate absorbs at a higher wavelength than the parent phenol. Linear titration curves

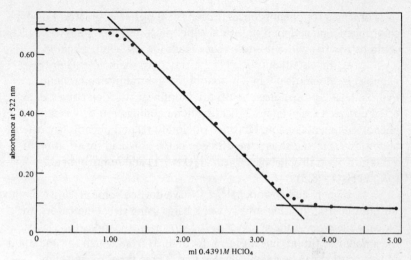

Figure 5.6 *Photometric titration of 2-methyl-5-nitroaniline and 4-methyl-2-nitroaniline in acetic acid. [Reprinted from L. E. I. Hummelstedt and D. N. Hume,* Anal. Chem., **32** *(1960): 576. Copyright 1960 by the American Chemical Society. Reprinted by permission of the copyright owner.]*

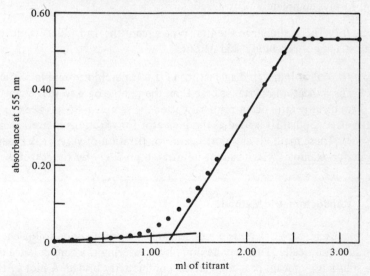

Figure 5.7 *Photometric titration of a mixture of p-nitrophenol and m-nitrophenol in 2-propanol. [Reprinted from L. E. I. Hummelstedt and D. N. Hume,* Anal. Chem., **32** *(1960): 1792. Copyright 1960 by the American Chemical Society. Reprinted by permission of the copyright owner.]*

69

were obtained for phenol concentrations of 0.001 M or greater. For p-chlorophenol-phenol and for several other mixtures, the more acidic phenol could be titrated without interference from the less acidic phenol.

Hummelstedt and Hume[24] titrated 16 weak acids (mostly phenols) photometrically in 2-propanol using tetrabutylammonium hydroxide in 2-propanol as the titrant. Nonlinear titration curves were often observed for phenols, indicating homoconjugation between the phenol and phenolate ion. Mixtures of closely related phenols can often be resolved. Fig. 5.7 shows the titration curve obtained for titration of a mixture of p-nitrophenol (pK_2 in H_2O = 7.1) and m-nitrophenol (pK_a in H_2O = 8.3).

Higuchi and coworkers[25-27] have devised some effective methods for photometric titration of very weak bases using visual indicators. By plotting the *ratio* of the acidic and basic forms of the indicator against the amount of titrant, linear plots are obtained from which the end point of the titration can be graphically located. Three types of plots are described:

Type I.   Plot Ind/IndH$^+$ vs. ml of 0.25 M perchloric acid. The indicator (quinaldine-red or malachite-green) is chosen so that conversion to the acid form is completely neutralized.

Type II.   This is similar to the first type except the Ind/IndH$^+$ is plotted against 1/ml of perchloric acid titrant.

Type III.   Plot IndH$^+$/Ind against ml of 0.1 M perchloric acid in acetic acid. The indicator is a weaker base than the sample base so that changes in the indicator ratio occur primarily after the sample base has been neutralized. Sudan III is used as the indicator for titrations in acetic acid.

These methods are most useful for titration of very weak bases (urea, for example) which cannot be titrated precisely by other techniques.

5.7   Conductometric Methods

Acid–base titrations in nonaqueous solvents may be followed conductometrically. This may be done by measuring the conductance of the solution by means of a commerical conductivity bridge. A plot of the conductance against volume of titrant added gives a curve that hopefully is linear with an inflection at the equivalence point. Similarly, a titration may be followed by means of a high-frequency oscillometer; and the titration tetrabutylammonium hydroxide.[31]

The shape of a conductometric titration curve depends on the mobility of the various ions in solution as well as on the pK of the substance titrated. In nonaqueous solvents the situation can become quite complicated and the shape of the curve difficult to predict in advance. Often the conductometric plot shows curvature in some places, and the linear portions do not show enough difference in slope to locate the equivalence point with precision. For these reasons, conductometric titration is only recommended for special studies or for the cases where this method gives results that compare favorably with potentiometric or other titration techniques.

In acetic acid solution conductometric titration of sulfuric acid with lithium acetate produces an "N-shaped" curve with sharp inflections when titration to the bisulfate and to the sulfate is complete.[28] The conductance increases as H_2SO_4 is converted to $Li^+HSO_4^-$, decreases when the lithium bisulfate is converted to lithium sulfate, and increases again when excess lithium acetate is added. Better results were obtained with lithium acetate titrant than with sodium or potassium acetate.

Extremely weak bases may be titrated conductometrically in the sulfuric acid solvent system.[29] Tetra (hydrogen sulphate) boric acid, $HB(HSO_4)_4$, is the acidic titrant. Bases react with the solvent to form the bisulfate ion, which is then titrated to form sulfuric acid:

$$Base + H_2SO_4 \rightleftarrows Base\ H^+ + HSO_4^-$$

$$HB(HSO_4)_4 + HSO_4^- \rightarrow B(HSO_4)_4^- + H_2SO_4$$

Bases titrated include potassium sulfate, aromatic and aliphatic ketones, aldehydes, and amides.

Acids may also be titrated conductometrically. The lower aliphatic dicarboxylic acids give excellent "N-shape" curves when titrated in dimethylformamide with tetramethylammonium hydroxide[30] or in pyridine or pyridine-benzene with tetrabutylammonium hydroxide.[31] Grove and Jeffery[32] titrated several acids successfully using high-frequency methods, but they concluded that there is no definite correlation between the high-frequency curve slopes and conductometric curves, the dielectric constant, or the basicity of the solvent.

5.8   Thermometric Methods

Keily and Hume[33] demonstrated that a wide variety of bases can be titrated in glacial acetic acid using thermometric indication of the end point. The titrations are carried out in a half-pint Dewar flask using a motor-driven syringe buret. The temperature is measured by a thermistor and Wheatstone bridge circuit. For best results, especially when very weak bases are titrated, the acetic acid solvent and the perchloric acid titrant should be anhydrous. Even very weak bases such as urea, acetamide and acetanilide, which are not amenable to direct titration by potentiometric methods, show a clearly defined end point when titrated thermometrically (see Fig. 5.8).

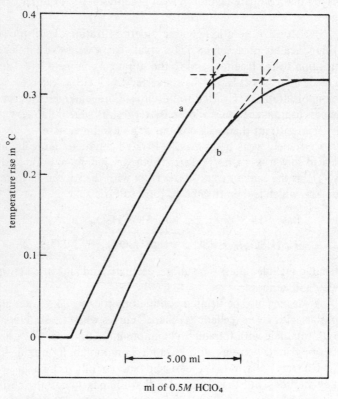

Figure 5.8 *Thermometric titration of very weak bases in acetic acid with anhydrous 0.5 M perchloric acid: (a) acetamide, (b) acetanilide. [Reprinted from H. J. Keiley and D. N. Hume, Anal. Chem., 36 (1964): 543. Copyright 1964 by the American Chemical Society. Reprinted by permission of the copyright owner.]*

Thermometric acid–base titrations have also been carried out in acetonitrile.[34] Bases were titrated using anhydrous hydrogen bromide in acetonitrile as the titrant. The instability of strong bases in acetonitrile greatly limits the practical application of this technique for the titration of acids. A comparatively weak base, diphenylguanidine, was used as the titrant; and only rather strong acids could be titrated.

PROBLEMS

1. What major advantage do metal or graphite electrodes have over the glass electrode for nonaqueous acid–base titrations? What disadvantage?

2. Explain how an anodized and a cathodized platinum electrode can each serve as a hydrogen ion indicator electrode. Write chemical equations for the oxidation–reduction half reactions of these electrodes with H^+.

3. Why is an aqueous salt bridge not recommended for the reference electrode used in the titration of acids in nonaqueous solvents? Give a more suitable salt bridge and specify a suitable physical arrangement for providing a good interface between the electrode and the test solution.

4. Explain why crystal violet has a much longer color transition range than most indicators when measured potentiometrically in terms of millivolts. How could the correct end-point color be chosen for particular titration?

5. Using Fig. 5.5, select a suitable indicator for titration of each of the acids in the mixture shown in Fig. 7.10.

6. (a) Tell how to select a suitable wavelength for the photometric titration of an aromatic amine without adding a visual indicator.
(b) A mixture of a base that does not absorb in the visible or UV spectral regions and a weaker aromatic amine is titrated photometrically. Sketch the titration curve and indicate where each of the two equivalence points will occur.
(c) Can a mixture of a non-absorbing base and a *stronger* aromatic amine be resolved by this type of photometric titration? Explain briefly.

7. Fig. 5.7 shows considerable curvature around the first equivalence point. Explain why this is so.

8. To avoid heat of mixing different solvents a thermometric titration requires that the titrant solvent be the same as the solvent used to dissolve the sample. Suggest a suitable titrant and solvent system that would be applicable for the thermometric titration of weak acids.

REFERENCES

1. C. W. Pifer, E. G. Wollish, and M. Schmall, *Anal. Chem.*, 25 (1953), 25, 310.
2. H. V. Malmstadt and E. R. Fett, *Anal. Chem.*, 26 (1954), 1348.
3. H. V. Malmstadt and D. A. Vassallo, *Anal. Chem.*, 31 (1959), 206, 862.
4. H. Zeidler, *Z. Anal. Chem.*, 146 (1955), 251.
5. G. Jander and H. Klaus, *J. Inorg. & Nuclear Chem.*, 1 (1955), 126, 228.
6. G. A. Harlow, C. M. Noble, and G. E. A. Wyld, *Anal. Chem.*, 28 (1956), 784.
7. I. Shain and G. R. Svoboda, *Anal. Chem.*, 11 (1959), 1857.
8. R. H. Cundiff and P. C. Markunas, *Anal. Chem.*, 28 (1956), 792.
9. L. W. Marple and J. S. Fritz, *Anal. Chem.*, 34 (1962), 796.
10. G. A. Harlow, *Anal. Chem.*, 34 (1962), 148.
11. J. S. Fritz, Mary McHugh, and M. Arguello (Unpublished work), 1971.
12. I. M. Kolthoff and T. B. Reddy, *Inorg. Chem.*, 1 (1962), 189.
13. M. Tezé and R. Schaal, *Bull. Chem. Soc. France*, 29 (1962), 1372.
14. M. E. Puthoff and J. H. Benedict, *Anal. Chem.*, 36 (1964), 2205.
15. C. A. Streuli, *Anal. Chem.*, 30 (1958), 997.
16. T. Higuchi, J. A. Feldman, and C. R. Rehm, *Anal. Chem.*, 28 (1956), 1120.
17. O. W. Kolling and M. L. Smith, *Anal. Chem.*, 31 (1959), 1876.
18. O. W. Kolling and T. L. Stevens, *Ibid.*, 33 (1961), 1384.
19. J. S. Fritz and F. E. Gainer, *Talanta*, 13 (1966), 939.
20. L. W. Marple and J. S. Fritz, *Anal. Chem.*, 35 (1963), 1305.
21. C. N. Reilley and B. Schweizer, *Anal. Chem.*, 26 (1954), 1124.
22. L. E. I. Hummelstedt and D. N. Hume, *Ibid.*, 32 (1960), 576.
23. R. W. McKinney and C. A. Reynolds, *Talanta*, 1 (1958), 46.
24. L. E. I. Hummelstedt and D. N. Hume, *Anal. Chem.*, 32 (1960), 1792.
25. K. A. Connors and T. Higuchi, *Anal. Chem.*, 32 (1960), 93.
26. T. Higuchi, C. Rehm, and R. Barnstein, *Ibid.*, 28 (1956), 1506.
27. C. Rehm and T. Higuchi, *Ibid.*, 29 (1957), 367.
28. T. Higuchi and C. R. Rehm, *Anal. Chem.*, 27 (1955), 408.
29. D. E. Leyden, D. L. Smith, and A. L. Underwood, *Anal. Chem.*, 35 (1963), 307.
30. N. Van Meurs and E. A. M. F. Dahmen, *Anal. Chim. Acta.*, 19 (1958), 64.
31. *Ibid.*, 21 (1959), 10, 443.
32. E. L. Grove and W. S. Jeffery, *Talanta*, 7 (1960), 56.
33. H. J. Keily and D. N. Hume, *Anal. Chem.*, 36 (1964), 543.
34. E. J. Forman and D. N. Hume, *Talanta*, 11 (1964), 129.

CHAPTER 6

Titration of Bases

The selecting of a suitable titrant and solvent was discussed in Chaps. 3 and 4. Methods for detecting the end point in a nonaqueous titration were covered in Chap. 5. For titrating an unknown or new type of base, potentiometric titration using glass and calomel electrodes is recommended with either manual or automatic plotting of the entire titration curve. If the end-point break (or breaks) is reasonably sharp, a visual indicator may be selected (see p. 64) and the correct color of the indicator ascertained at the equivalence point. A visual indicator is recommended for routine titrations performed manually because it is faster and requires less manipulation than manual potentiometric titrations. Titrimeters are available that titrate automatically to a given indicator color change or to a predetermined potential of electrodes in the solution.

It is convenient to use the ionization constants that have been determined in aqueous solution for various bases to predict the relative strengths of these bases when titrated in a nonaqueous solvent. A large number of pK_b values have been measured for bases in water but relatively few such data are available for nonaqueous solvents. Hall and Werner[1] and Streuli[2] have shown that a linear relationship exists when the half-neutralization potential (HNP) in millivolts for a series of bases titrated in an organic solvent is plotted against the pK values in water (Fig. 6.1). (This holds only for bases that are not leveled by a particular solvent.) There are exceptions of course, but the linear relationship appears to be a good approximation for most compounds. This means that the titration behavior of a base in a nonaqueous solvent may be predicted from its dissociation constant in aqueous solution. Perrin[3] lists dissociation constants in water for approximately 3800 bases, so the scope of predictions is obviously broad.

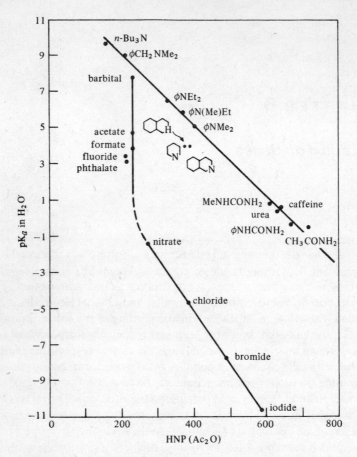

Figure 6.1 *Half-neutralization potential (mv) in acetic anhydride solution as a function of pK_a of protonated bases in water. [Reprinted from C. A. Streuli,* Anal. Chem., **30** *(1958): 997. Copyright 1958 by the American Chemical Society. Reprinted by permission of the copyright owner.]*

The slope of this type of a plot is often greater than 59 mv/pK_b, which is the slope of a plot in water of HNP (mv) vs. pK_b. For example, Streuli[2] obtained a slope of 78 mv/pK_b for titration of a series of bases in nitromethane. This means that the difference in HNP for any two bases will be greater in nitromethane than in aqueous solution, and the chances of resolving a mixture of the bases (that is, obtaining separate end points) will be better in nitromethane. A titration in which a mixture of two or more bases (or acids) is resolved with a distinguishable end point for each base will be referred to as a *differentiating titration*.

In this chapter we shall indicate which types of bases can be titrated, the general conditions for titration, and the effect of structural variations on the titration. In addition to the literature references cited in the following sections, Ashworth[4] lists in tabular form some 341 literature references with conditions for titrations of bases in nonaqueous solvents with perchloric acid titrant.

6.1 Determination of Total Base

Amines

The most widely applicable method for organic bases involves titration with standard perchloric acid dissolved in either glacial acetic acid or 1,4-dioxane. The base to be titrated is dissolved in acetic acid, nitromethane, acetonitrile, chlorobenzene, benzene, chloroform, carbon tetrachloride, or some other nonbasic solvent. The end point is determined either potentiometrically or by a visual indicator such as methyl violet.

By this method, primary, secondary, and tertiary amines and amino acids can be determined. Some amino acids are difficult to dissolve in acetic acid and are, therefore, dissolved in acetic acid containing a measured amount of perchloric acid. The excess perchloric acid is then back-titrated with a standard base such as potassium acetate in glacial acetic acid.

Aromatic amines are quite weak bases in water (pK_b in water for aniline is 9.4) but can be accurately titrated in acetic acid. Chloro, bromo, nitro, and certain other electron-withdrawing groups decrease the basic strength of aromatic amines, especially if the substituents are in the *ortho* or *para* positions. Alkyl substituents tend to enhance the basic strength of amines slightly. Fig. 6.2 shows the effect of various substituents on the

TABLE 6.1
Effect of Various Substituents on the Basic Strength of Aniline

Substituent	pK_b in Water	ΔpK_b
None	9.4	0.0
o-NO$_2$	13.9	+4.5
o-X(Cl, Br)	11.3	+1.9
m-X(Cl, Br)	10.5	+1.1
p-NO$_2$	12.1	+2.7
p-SO$_2$NH$_2$	11.7	+2.3
p-COCH$_3$	11.3	+1.9
p-X(Cl, Br)	10.1	+0.7

titration of aromatic amines. It will be noted that amines having a pK_b in water less than 12.0 to 12.5 are strong enough to be titrated potentiometrically in glacial acetic acid. Table 6.1 lists the pK_b values for a number of aniline derivatives along with the number of units that each group raises the pK_b. If, as a rough approximation, the effect of each

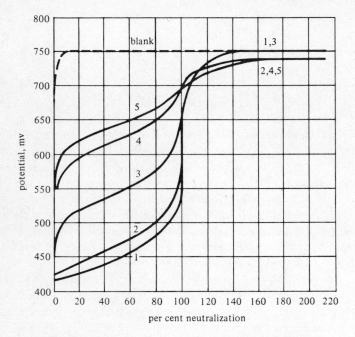

Figure 6.2 *Titration of amines in acetic acid with 0.1 M perchloric acid measured with glass-calomel electrodes: (1) aniline, pK_b in $H_2O = 9.4$; (2) p-bromoaniline, pK_b in $H_2O = 10.1$; (3) o-chloroaniline, pK_b in $H_2O = 11.2$; (4) p-nitroaniline, pK_b in $H_2O = 12.1$; (5) quinoxaline, pK_b in $H_2O = 13.2$.*

group is assumed to be additive, it is possible to predict whether a given amine can be titrated. For example, by adding 1.9 pK units for an *ortho* halogen and 0.7 unit for a *para* halogen to the pK_b for aniline (9.4), the pK_b for 2,4-dichloroaniline is calculated to be 12.0. The measured pK_b is 12.2. From this it would be predicted that 2,4-dichloroaniline is a sufficiently strong base to be titrated in acetic acid. This procedure and its limitations are presented in detail in discussions of the Hammett equation.[5,6]

TABLE 6.2

Ionization Constants (in Water) of Nitrogen Heterocyclic Bases

Formula	Name	pK_b (in H_2O)
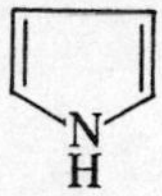	Pyrrole	> 16
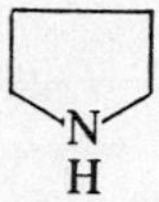	Pyrrolidine	2.9
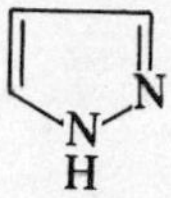	Pyrazole	11.5
	Thiazole	11.5
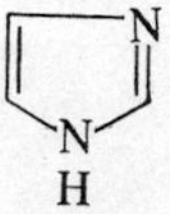	Imidazole	7.0
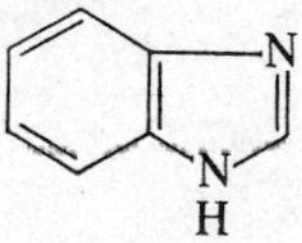	Benzimidazole	8.5
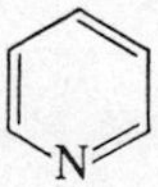	Pyridine	8.8
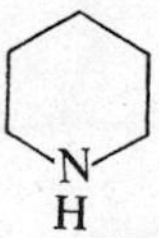	Piperidine	2.8
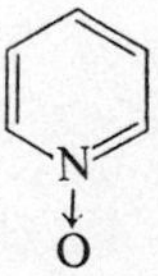	Pyridine-N-oxide	13.2
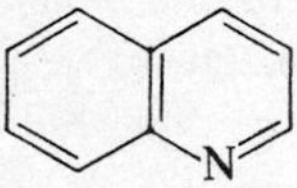	Quinoline	8.9

TABLE 6.2 (*Continued*)

Formula	Name	pK_b in H_2O
	Isoquinoline	8.7
	Pyridazine	11.7
	Pyrimidine	12.7
	Pyrazine	13.4
	Quinoxaline	13.2
	Caffeine	13.4

Effect of Water

Most amines can be titrated in acetic acid containing up to 2 or 3% water. If more water is present, the end point is not sharp and the results would be somewhat inaccurate. Alcohol has a similar effect but can be tolerated in somewhat larger amounts because it is less basic than water. An aqueous solution of a base can be handled in one of two ways. If the solution is sufficiently concentrated, a small measured portion can be diluted with about a fifty-fold excess of acetic acid and titrated directly. Or, the base can be extracted with an immiscible solvent such as benzene or chloroform. Automatic continuous extractors are available which make this a convenient operation. The base is then titrated directly in the extracting solvent.

Nitrogen Heterocyclic Compounds

Many nitrogen heterocyclics are sufficiently basic to be titrated in nonaqueous solvents. In general bases of pK_b in water $\leqq 12$ can be titrated potentiometrically in acetic acid, nitromethane, etc. Bases stronger than $pK_b = 10$ or 11 may be titrated accurately using a visual indicator.

Table 6.2 lists the pK_b values (in water) of several parent hetero-cyclic compounds, arranged according to structure. From these and other data several useful generalities may be deduced regarding the basicity of nitro heterocyclics.

1. A second hetero atom in the ring decreases the basicity significantly.
2. A fused aromatic ring further reduces the basicity (compare imidazole and benzimidazole).
3. Electron-withdrawing substituents in the ring such as $-Cl$, $-NO_2$, and $-CN$ decrease the basicity while alkyl substituents *increase* the bascity.
4. Complete saturation of the ring converts the compound to a cycloaliphatic amine which is a much stronger base (compare pyridine and piperidine).

Salts

Salts of weak acids, A^-, can be titrated with a strong acid.

$$H^+ClO_4^- + A^- \rightarrow HA + ClO_4^-$$

In aqueous solution only the salts of very weak acids (weaker than $pK_a \sim 6$) can be titrated in this way. In alcoholic solvents and especially in solvent mixtures containing glycol ("G-H" solvent) alkali metal salts of carboxylic acids may be accurately titrated.[7] In glacial acetic acid the alkali metal and amine salts of carboxylic acids, and even some "strong" mineral acids, may be successfully titrated. For example, amine nitrates are titrated to nitric acid (which is a fairly weak acid in acetic acid solution) as a neutralization product, and sulfates are titrated to bisulfates.

$$H^+ClO_4^- + RNH_3^+NO_3^- \rightarrow RNH_3^+ClO_4^- + H^+NO_3^-$$

$$H^+ClO_4^- + (RNH_3^+)_2SO_4^= \rightarrow RNH_3^+ClO_4^- + RNH_3^+HSO_4^-$$

(It may be recalled from Chap. 2 that salts in acetic acid exist largely as ion pairs.)

An ingenious modification introduced by Pifer and Wollish[8] permits the titration of amine halide salts, which are too weakly basic to be titrated directly in acetic acid. This titration is made possible by first adding mercuric acetate to convert the halide (X^-) to undissociated HgX_2 and then titrating the amine acetate with standard perchloric acid.

$$2RNH_3^+X^- + HgAc_2 \rightarrow 2RNH_3^+Ac^- + HgX_2$$

$$H^+ClO_4^- + RNH_3^+Ac^- \rightarrow RNH_3^+ClO_4^- + HAc$$

Mercuric acetate is undissociated in acetic acid and does not interfere in the titration if a modest excess is used. The method is applicable to amine salts of hydrochloric, hydrobromic, and hydriodic acid. Some dioxane mixed with the acetic acid enhances the sharpness of the potentiometric end point, particularly, if titrant is as dilute as 0.01 M. For this reason perchloric acid in dioxane is the recommended titrant.

Direct titration of amine salts is especially important in the pharmaceutical industry because it permits assay of the total amine content of a drug whether it is present as the free amine or as the salt. A small excess of acid (HX) will not interfere in the amine titration because it is converted to acetic acid by the mercuric acetate.

$$2H^+X^- + HgAc_2 \rightarrow HgX_2 + 2HAc$$

Quaternary ammonium salts may also be titrated according to the methods just described.

Although soluble alkali metal salts may be titrated as bases in acetic acid, salts of polyvalent metal ions are associated in acetic acid and give shorter potentiometric breaks, or cannot be titrated at all. However, Casey and Starke[9] reported the successful titration of acetates of 15 metal ions and the chloroacetates of 4 metal ions. Titration in a solvent mixture containing acetonitrile greatly improves the titration of several metal acetates, due to strong solvation of the metal ion with accompanying liberation of acetate ions.[10]

Epoxides

Epoxides act as a special type of base by virtue of their ability to react with hydrohalides.

$$-CH\underset{O}{-}CH_2 + HX \longrightarrow -CH\underset{\underset{X}{|}}{-}CH_2OH$$

In acetic acid, the reaction of terminal epoxides with a solution of anhydrous hydrogen bromide in acetic acid is rapid enough for the epoxide to be titrated directly.[11] The end point of the titration is determined with crystal violet indicator or by ordinary potentiometric means. Epoxides can be determined in the presence of peroxides, hydro-peroxides, carboxylic acids, aldehydes, alcohols, esters, glycols, or olefins.

Amines, if present in the sample, give a separate potentiometric end point before the epoxide is titrated.

A clever modification of this method permits direct titration of interior epoxides, which react more slowly than terminal epoxides, and uses a more conveniently prepared titrant, perchloric acid in glacial acetic acid. The addition of hydrogen bromide to an epoxide involves a rapid protonation, followed by a slower step in which bromide is added.

$$-CH-CH-_{\backslash O/} \; + \; H^+ \; \underset{}{\overset{fast}{\rightleftharpoons}} \; \left(\begin{array}{c} -CH-CH- \\ \backslash O / \\ H \end{array}\right)^+ \; + \; Br^- \; \underset{}{\overset{slower}{\rightleftharpoons}} \; \begin{array}{c} -CH-CH- \\ | \quad | \\ Br \quad OH \end{array}$$

The rapid protonation step is achieved through the perchloric acid titrant. The addition step is accomplished by an excess of a quaternary ammonium halide added to the solution before the actual titration with perchloric acid. The excess of the halide salt is sufficient to speed up the addition step so that the overall reaction is quite rapid. Dijkstra and Dahmen[12] use cetyltrimethylammonium bromide while Jay[13] recommends either tetraethylammonium bromide in acetic acid or tetrabutylammonium iodide in chloroform.

Very Weak Bases

1. *Titration in solvents containing acetic anhydride.* For titration of bases weaker than about pK_b in H_2O = 10 (and especially for those weaker than pK_b in $H_2O \sim 12$), a very definite improvement in the end point can be obtained by titrating in acetic acid, nitromethane or aceto-nitrile containing 5 to 20% by volume of acetic anhydride[14] or in acetic anhydride alone.[15] The maximum potential attainable when excess perchloric acid has been added is at least 100 mv greater when excess acetic anhydride is mixed with the solvent. Titrations in which acetic anhydride is present exclude primary and secondary amines because of the ease with which they are acetylated. In certain cases, however, acetylation can be avoided by titrating at a low temperature.

The complete removal of water, which is a weak base, by acetic anhydride accounts for part of the improvement in the titrations. However, there is evidence that perchloric acid is converted to $(CH_3CO)^+$ in acetic anhydride, which is a stronger acid even than anhydrous perchloric acid.

$$(CH_3CO)_2O + HClO_4 \rightarrow CH_3CO^+ClO_4^- + CH_3CO_2H$$

Although most amides are too weakly basic to be titrated in acetic acid, Wimer[16] was able to titrate some 41 amides of various types in acetic anhydride solvent. The amides are titrated with perchloric acid in acetic acid, and the titration is followed potentiometrically using a glass-calomel electrode system. The aqueous potassium chloride in the calomel electrode is replaced with a 0.1 M solution of anhydrous lithium perchlorate in acetic anhydride.

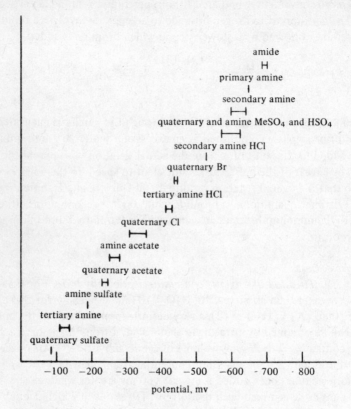

Figure 6.3 *Half-neutralization potential ranges of salts in acetic anhydride. [Reprinted from M. E. Puthoff and J. H. Benedict, Anal. Chem., 36 (1964): 2205. Copyright 1964 by the American Chemical Society. Reprinted by permission of the copyright owner.]*

Berger and Uldall[17] obtained low results for primary amides using Wimer's method. Pietrzyk[18] also obtained low results for titration of acetamide in 90% acetic anhydride–10% acetic acid, the error increasing as the time for titration increased. Wimer[19] later reported that primary amides may be titrated accurately at 0°C, an observation in agreement with Gremillion[20] who titrated urea in acetic anhydride at low temperature. Pietrzyk[18] avoided acetylation of acetamide by titrating with trinitrobenzenesulfonic acid instead of perchloric acid.

Dialkyl sulfoxides[15, 21] and phosphine oxides[15, 22] have also been titrated as bases in acetic anhydride solvent mixtures. Fritz and Fulda[14] successfully determined triphenylcarbinol and several nitrogen heterocyclics as bases in nitromethane-acetic anhydride. Hennart and Merlin[23] titrated benzimidazole in propionic acid containing propionic anhydride.

Amine oxides, which are also very weak bases, have been determined by titration in acetic anhydride.[24-25]

Quaternary ammonium salts, even chlorides and bromides, may be directly titrated as bases in acetic anhydride.[15,26] The relative basicity of various salts is indicated by the half-neutralization potentials shown in Fig. 6.3.

2. *Titration in dichloroacetic acid.* Schaal[27] titrated some extremely weak bases in anhydrous dichloroacetic acid with perchloric acid in the same solvent. The chloranil indicator electrode was used in obtaining potentiometric titration curves. Acetanilide and even water was titrated as a base. Because of the acidic nature of dichloroacetic acid, most bases are leveled to the basic strength of the dichloroacetate ion.

3. *Spectrophotometric titrations.* Weak bases may be titrated spectrophotometrically either by utilizing the absorption spectrum of the basic or acidic form of the substance titrated, or by following the absorbance of an added visual indicator. Reilley and Schweitzer,[28] and Hummelstedt and Hume[29] titrated weak bases in acetic acid with perchloric acid. They made use of the fact that aromatic amines absorb light in the ultraviolet region, and that the absorption maxima of the free base and protonated base occur at different wavelengths. Several mixtures were titrated that could not be resolved by potentiometric titration (see Fig. 5.6, for example). Bases as weak as p-nitroaniline (pK_b in H_2O = 13.0) and 4-methyl-2-nitroaniline (pK_b in H_2O = 13.5) may be titrated in essentially anhydrous acetic acid, although the curves in the vicinity of the equivalence point are somewhat rounded. o-Nitroaniline (pK_b in H_2O = 14.3) is too weakly basic to be titrated under these conditions.

The photometric titration methods developed by Higuchi *et al.*[30,31] are useful for the quantitative determination of quite weak bases. Urea may be titrated accurately with perchloric acid in acetic acid using malachite-green or nile-blue indicator in a type II plot[30] or with sudan III in a type III plot[31] (see p. 70).

4. *Thermometric titrations.* Keiley and Hume[32] applied the automatic thermometric titration method (p. 72) to the titration of bases

in glacial acetic acid. Under strictly anhydrous conditions even the very weak bases diphenylamine, urea, acetamide, and acetanilide are readily titratable. Anhydrous conditions are obtained by adding the exact theoretical amount of acetic anhydride to combine with the water in both the solvent and the perchloric acid.

6.2 Analysis of Mixtures

Two approaches are used for the quantitative differentiation of amines in mixtures: One approach is to do a titration in which separate end points are obtained for amines of different basic strength. The other is

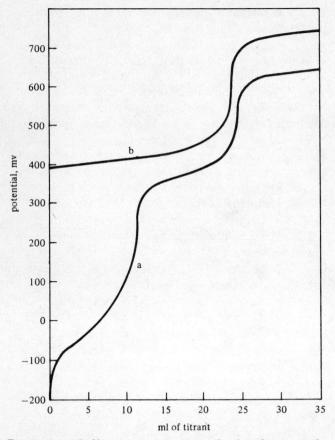

Figure 6.4 *Differentiating titration of tributylamine and N-ethylaniline in acetonitrile (curve A). Curve B is for titration of the same mixture in acetic acid.*

to distinguish quantitatively between primary, secondary, and tertiary amines.

In water the pK_b of aliphatic amines is ordinarily about 4 or 5, and pK_b of aromatic amines is 9 or greater. This is enough difference to permit sharp, separate end points for aliphatic and aromatic amines in a mixture. Because aromatic amines are too weakly basic to be titrated in water, a nonaqueous solvent must be used if the mixture is to be analyzed by a single, differentiating titration. However, a typical aliphatic-aromatic amine mixture titrated in acetic acid gives only a single inflection in the titration curve, corresponding to the titration of the total amine present. This may be attributed to the leveling effect of acetic acid. The aliphatic amine reacts with the solvent to form the amine acetate.

$$RNH_2 + HAc \rightarrow RNH_3^+Ac^-$$

Therefore it is the acetate rather than the free aliphatic amine that is titrated with perchloric acid. Acetate has about the same basic strength as the aromatic amine, hence only one end point is observed in the titration.

A mixture of aliphatic and aromatic amines can be titrated in a solvent such as acetonitrile,[33] chloroform,[34] or acetone.[35] These solvents do not level the amines because they are not acidic; however, they permit the accurate titration of the aromatic amine which water or alcohol solvents do not. The titration is performed with perchloric acid in dioxane rather than in acetic acid. Titration curves for a typical mixture in acetic acid and in acetonitrile are shown in Fig. 6.4. Titration of ethylenediamine in acetone shows a separate break for each nitrogen (Fig. 6.5).

Two aromatic amines in mixtures can be differentiated in acetic acid provided there is sufficient difference in the basic strength of the amines. Acetic acid will not level amines less basic than pK_b (in water) of about 9.3.

The photometric titration method of Hummelstedt and Hume[29] seems ideally suited to the differentiating titration of mixtures of aromatic amines (see p. 68).

Primary, secondary, and tertiary amines can be distinguished quantitatively by acidimetric titrations. Tertiary amines are determined after first acetylating primary and secondary amines with acetic anhydride. This method was first proposed by Blumrich and Bandel[36] and further developed by Wagner, Brown and Peters.[37] Acetylated primary and secondary amines are hardly basic at all, but tertiary amines are unaffected and can be titrated with perchloric acid. The excess acetic anhydride does not interfere with the titration; in many cases, it actually improves the end point.

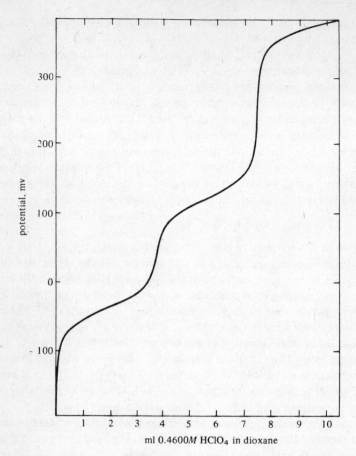

Fig. 6.5 *Titration of ethylenediamine in acetone.*

The acetic anhydride method measures tertiary amines directly and primary plus secondary amines by difference. The sum of primary and secondary amines can be determined directly by reaction with carbon disulfide in pyridine-isopropyl alcohols to form dithiocarbamic acids.

$$RNH_2 + CS_2 \rightarrow RNH\overset{\displaystyle S}{\overset{\displaystyle \|}{C}}-SH$$

$$R_2NH + CS_2 \rightarrow R_2N\overset{\displaystyle S}{\overset{\displaystyle \|}{C}}-SH$$

The dithiocarbamic acids are then titrated with 0.5 N aqueous sodium hydroxide.[38]

Several methods have been proposed for the differentiation of primary and secondary amines. A widely used method is based on the reaction of primary amines with salicylaldehyde to form a Schiff base.

The Schiff base is considerably weaker than the original amine (approximate pK_b in water for RNH_2 = 4; approximate pK_b for the Schiff base = 9). Secondary and tertiary amines retain their original basic strength. The difference in titrations of the stronger base before and after reaction with salicylaldehyde measures the amount of primary amine present.

Wagner, Brown, and Peters[39] use benzene-isopropyl alcohol solvent for acid–base titrations in the salicylaldehyde method for primary aliphatic amines. Siggia, Hanna, and Kervenski[40] use glycol-isopropyl alcohol solution and claim to have analyzed aromatic as well as aliphatic amine mixtures. Perhaps, the most convenient method is that of Critchfield and Johnson.[41] They react the primary amine in an aliphatic amine mixture with salicylaldehyde in chloroform for 15 minutes. Then, the secondary plus tertiary amine is titrated to a bromocresol-green end point with 0.5 N perchloric acid in dioxane. At this point more dioxane is added, and the titration is continued to the congo-red end point. The difference between the two end points represents the titration of the Schiff base of the primary amine. Ammonia, morpholine, and ethanolamines interfere; and the method is not applicable to aromatic amine mixtures.

In acetic acid Gal'pern and Bezinger[42] found that only primary amines react with phthalic anhydride. The secondary plus tertiary amines are then titrated with perchloric acid. Acetic anhydride in acetic acid reacts with both primary and secondary amines, and the tertiary amine is titrated with perchloric acid. These determinations along with a titration for the total amine permit a complete analysis of amine mixtures. The method is said to be applicable to mixtures of aromatic or aliphatic amines.

The analysis of mixtures of primary, secondary, and tertiary amines containing both aliphatic and aromatic amines poses a problem. The Schiff bases of primary aliphatic and aromatic amines are each weaker than the parent amine, and, of course, the various aromatic amines are in turn weaker than the aliphatic. The titration curve for many mixtures that have been treated with salicylaldehyde may be predicted from the following constants of bases in water:

$$1°, 2°, 3° \text{ aliphatic}, pK_b \sim 4$$

$$1° \text{ aliphatic Schiff base}, pK_b \sim 9$$

$$1°, 2°, 3° \text{ aromatic}, pK_b \sim 9 - 12$$

$$1° \text{ aromatic Schiff base}, pK_b \sim 11 - 12$$

Thus, a mixture of RNH_2, $ArNH_2$, and pyridine ($pK_b = 8.8$) after reaction with salicylaldehyde produces two breaks when titrated with perchloric acid: The first is pyridine plus RNH_2 Schiff base; the second is for $ArNH_2$ Schiff base.

    Huber[43] found that Schiff bases of primary aromatic amines (but not aliphatic) are unreactive towards acetic anhydride. Therefore, a mixture containing $ArNH_2$, R_2NH (or ArNHR), and R_3N (or $ArNR_2$) may be analyzed for primary plus tertiary amine by reaction with salicylaldehyde, followed by acetylation (of the secondary amine) and titration with perchloric acid. A scheme for complete analysis of this mixture would be as follows:

(a)   Titrate total base, $1° + 2° + 3°$, in acetic acid.

(b)   Salicylaldehyde (15 min), then acetic anhyd. (10 min), then titrate $1° + 2°$.

(c)   Acetic anhyd. (10 min), then titrate $3°$.
       Primary amine = (b) − (c), secondary amine = (a) − (b), tertiary amine = (c).

PROBLEMS

1.   Outline conditions for titrating each of the following compounds as a base in a nonaqueous solvent.

(a)

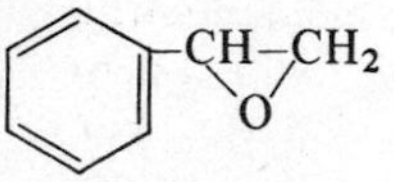

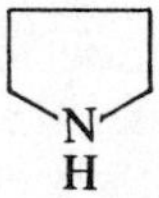

(b) $CH_3CON(C_2H_5)_2$

(c)

(d)

(e) CH_3CHCO_2H
        $|$
       NH_2

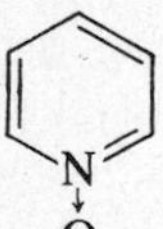

(f)

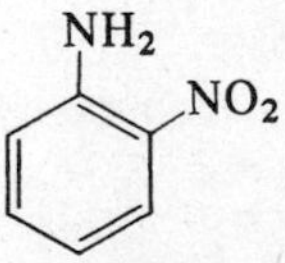

2. Using acid–base titration, outline a scheme for quantitative analysis of each of the following mixtures.

   (a)

   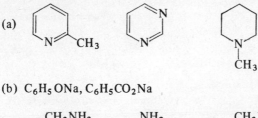

   (b) C_6H_5ONa, $C_6H_5CO_2Na$

   (c)

   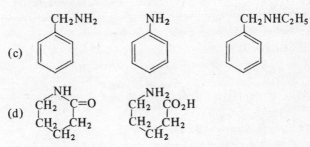

   (d)

3. For each of the following indicate the type of titration curve that will be obtained in acetone using perchloric acid in dioxane as the titrant.

   (a)

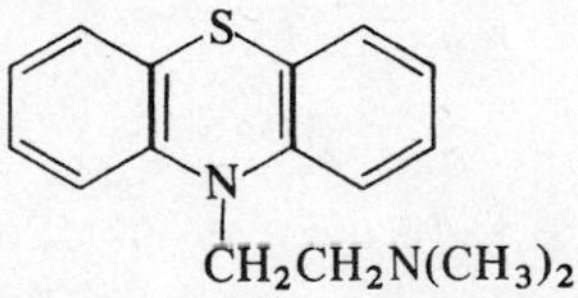

   (b) $NH_2CH_2CH_2NH_2$

4. Procaine, $H_2NC_6H_5CO_2CH_2CH_2N(C_2H_5)_2$, is often used as the the hydrochloride, nitrate or borate salt, but the anesthetic activity is proportional to the amount of the parent base. Suggest a titrimetric method for the assay of procaine hydrochloride.

5. Suggest a possible analytical method for determination of carbon disulfide based on its reaction with an excess of a secondary aliphatic amine. Write chemical equations for the reactions involved and indicate clearly the plan of the method.

REFERENCES

1. N. F. Hall and T. H. Werner, *J. Am. Chem. Soc.*, **50** (1928), 2367.
2. C. A. Streuli, *Anal. Chem.*, **31** (1959), 1652; *Ibid.*, **30** (1958), 997.
3. D. D. Perrin, *Dissociation Constants of Organic Bases in Aqueous Solution*, London: Butterworths, 1965.
4. M. R. F. Ashworth, *Titrimetric Organic Analysis. I. Direct Methods*, New York: Wiley-Interscience, 1964.

5.   L. P. Hammett, *Physical Organic Chemistry*, New York: McGraw-Hill Book Co., 1940, pp. 186–194.

6.   H. H. Jaffe, *Chem. Revs.* **53** (1953), 191.

7.   S. R. Palit, *Ind. Eng. Chem., Anal. Ed.*, **18** (1946), 246.

8.   C. W. Pifer and E. G. Wollish, *Anal. Chem.*, **24** (1952), 300.

9.   A. T. Casey and K. Starke, *Anal. Chem.*, **31** (1959), 1060.

10.   J. S. Fritz, *Anal. Chem.*, **26** (1954), 1701.

11.   A. J. Durbetaki, *Anal. Chem.*, **28** (1956), 2000.

12.   R. Dijkstra and E. A. M. F. Dahmen, *Anal. Chim. Acta*, **31** (1964), 38.

13.   R. R. Jay, *J. Am. Chem. Soc.*, **36** (1964), 667.

14.   J. S. Fritz and M. O. Fulda, *Anal. Chem.*, **25** (1953), 1837.

15.   C. A. Streuli, *Anal. Chem.*, **30** (1958), 997.

16.   D. C. Wimer, *Anal. Chem.*, **30** (1958), 77.

17.   J. Berger and I. Uldall, *Acta Chem. Scand.*, **18** (1964), 1311.

18.   D. J. Pietrzyk, *Anal. Chem.*, **39** (1967), 1367.

19.   D. C. Wimer, *Talanta*, **13** (1966), 1472.

20.   A. F. Gremillion, *Anal. Chem.*, **27** (1955), 133.

21.   D. C. Wimer, *Anal. Chem.*, **30** (1958), 2060.

22.   J. R. Parker and C. V. Banks, *Anal. Chem.*, **36** (1964), 2191.

23.   C. Hennart and E. Merlin, *Chim. Anal.*, **40** (1958), 264.

24.   D. C. Wimer, *Anal. Chem.*, **34** (1962), 873.

25.   C. W. Muth, R. S. Darlak, W. H. English, and A. T. Hamner, *Anal. Chem.*, **34** (1962), 1163.

26.   M. E. Puthoff and J. H. Benedict, *Anal. Chem.*, **36** (1964), 2205.

27.   R. Schaal, Thesis, Univ. of Paris, 1956.

28.   C. N. Reilley and B. Schweitzer, *Anal. Chem.*, **26** (1954), 1124.

29.   L. E. I. Hummelstedt and D. N. Hume, *Anal. Chem.*, **32** (1960), 576.

30.   T. Higuchi, C. Rehm, and R. Barnstein, *Anal. Chem.*, **28** (1956), 1506.

31.   C. Rehm and T. Higuchi, *Anal. Chem.*, **29** (1957), 367.

32.   H. J. Keiley and D. N. Hume, *Anal. Chem.*, **36** (1964), 543.

33.   J. S. Fritz, *Anal. Chem.*, **25** (1953), 407.

34.   C. W. Pifer, E. G. Wollish, and M. Schmall, *Anal. Chem.*, **25** (1953), 310.

35.   J. S. Fritz and C. A. Burgett, *Anal. Chem.*, **44** (1972), 1673.

36.   K. G. Blumrich and G. Bandel, *Angew. Chem.*, **54** (1941), 374.

37.   C. D. Wagner, R. H. Brown, and E. D. Peters, *J. Am. Chem. Soc.*, **69** (1947), 2609.

38.   F. E. Critchfield and J. B. Johnson, *Anal. Chem.*, **28** (1956), 430.

39.   C. D. Wagner, R. H. Brown, and E. D. Peters, *J. Am. Chem. Soc.*, **69** (1947), 2611.

REFERENCES

40. S. Siggia, J. G. Hanna, and I. R. Kervenski, *Anal. Chem.*, **22** (1950), 1295.
41. F. E. Critchfield and J. B. Johnson, *Anal. Chem.*, **29** (1957), 957.
42. G. D. Gal'pern and N. N. Bezinger, *J. Anal. Chem.* (U.S.S.R.), (English Translation), **13** (1958), 679.
43. W. Huber, *Titrations in Nonaqueous Solvents*, New York: Academic Press, 1967, p. 127.

CHAPTER 7

Titration of Acids

Many types of organic acids are sufficiently acidic to be titrated in nonaqueous solvents. The order of acidity of uncharged acids is usually the same in nonaqueous solvents as in water, hence the pK_a values in aqueous solution are a valuable guide to whether a given acid will be titratable and to the type of titration curve that will be obtained. With a quaternary ammonium hydroxide or alkali metal alkoxide titrant, compounds having a pK_a in H_2O up to approximately 10 are titratable with good precision and accuracy in a suitable nonaqueous solvent. Titration of acids having pK_a in H_2O from 10 to 11 is somewhat marginal. In a complete anhydrous solvent of the proper type, extremely weak acids (alcohols, for example) may be titrated with a very strongly basic titrant such as sodium dimethylsulfoxide.

Kortum, Vogel, and Andrussow[1] list pK_a values for some 1056 organic acids in aqueous solution. The listings for carboxylic acids and phenols are extensive. However, comparatively few dissociation constants are given for other types of organic acids, many of which are sparingly soluble in water. For these it is convenient to correlate the chemical structure with the titration curve obtained when the compound is titrated in a nonaqueous solvent. This type of information enables predictions to be made regarding the titratability of new compounds.

In this chapter titration of the various classes of acids is discussed in alphabetical order. Whenever possible the general effects of substituents and other structural variations on the strength of an acid will be pointed out. Following this, a section on the determination of acids by coulometric titration is presented. Then, titration of mixtures is discussed; and finally, there is a short section on methods for titration of very weak acids.

The selection of a solvent, titrant, and method for locating the equivalence point of a titration was discussed in Chaps. 3, 4, and 5, respectively. A non-acidic and relatively polar solvent such as dimethylformamide, t-butyl alcohol, or acetone is recommended for titration of most acids. In general, a quaternary ammonium hydroxide, usually tributylmethylammonium or tetrabutylammonium hydroxide, is the most satisfactory titrant for acids. For best results the titrant used should be free from weakly basic impurities such as carbonate and tertiary amines. If such impurities do remain in the titrant their possible effect on the titration of a particular acid should be considered and an appropriate blank subtracted from the buret reading of the actual titration. The amount of titrant impurities that needs to be subtracted in any given potential range may be determined by titration of a portion of the quaternary ammonium titrant with a strong acid (See Fig. 4.1).

Potentiometric titration curves are widely used in the following sections to describe titration of various types of acids. Once the general characteristics of a particular titration are known, a suitable visual indicator can usually be selected (see Chap. 5). For routine titrations the use of visual indicators is usually more rapid and convenient than potentiometric titration.

7.1   Determination of Various Acids

Carboxylic Acids

Simple carboxylic acids are acidic enough (pK_a in H_2O = 4 to 5) that titration presents no difficulty. Titration in aqueous or alcoholic solution with aqueous sodium hydroxide using phenolphthalein indicator is a familiar procedure. However, a longer potentiometric break and a sharper end point is obtained when the acid is titrated in 2-propanol, t-butyl alcohol, pyridine, dimethylformamide, or acetone with tetrabutylammonium hydroxide. In pyridine or acetone the acid anion combines with the free acid to form a complex during the early stages of the titration.

$$A^- + HA \rightarrow AHA^-$$

This increases the slope of the titration curve in the buffer region and reduces the magnitude of the end-point break somewhat. Such homoconjugation effects are not encountered when a carboxylic acid is titrated in an alcohol or dimethylformamide, which have excellent solvating properties.

95

Amino acids are much weaker than ordinary carboxylic acids. For example, glycine, $H_2N-CH_2-CO_2H$, has a pK_a in H_2O = 9.8 at 25°C. These acids form zwitterions ($H_3\overset{+}{N}-CH_2CO_2^-$, for example) and are soluble only in water or in highly polar organic solvents. Cundiff and Markunas[2] titrated amino acids in pyridine with tetrabutylammonium hydroxide after first dissolving the acid in the minimum amount of water.

Dicarboxylic acids often give a separate potentiometric break for each of the carboxyl groups. A nearby carboxyl group enhances the acidity

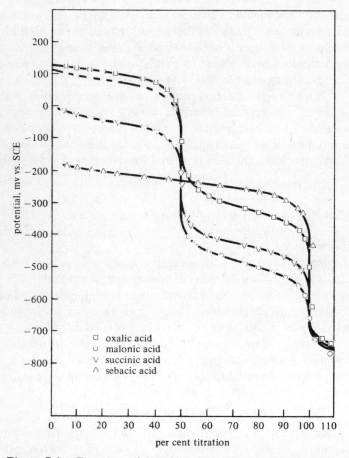

Figure 7.1 *Titration of dicarboxylic acids in* t-*butyl alcohol with tetrabutylammonium hydroxide. [Reprinted from J. S. Fritz and L. W. Marple,* Anal. Chem., **34** *(1962): 921. Copyright 1962 by the American Chemical Society. Reprinted by permission of the copyright owner.]*

of the other carboxyl group. When the first carboxylic acid group has been neutralized to form a carboxylate anion, however, the inductive properties reduce the acidity of the second, neighboring group. In molecules where the two carboxylic acid groups are more widely separated, their effect on each other diminishes. These effects are illustrated in Fig. 7.1. The aliphatic dicarboxylic acids through succinic acid, $HO_2C(CH_2)_2CO_2H$, show two distinct breaks. In sebacic acid, $HO_2C(CH_2)_8CO_2H$, where the carboxyl groups are more widely separated, the carboxyl groups act independently of each other; and the only break in the titration curve is when both groups have been titrated.

Harlow and Wyld[3] studied the effect of water on titration of dicarboxylic acids in 2-propanol. Jasinski and Smagowski[4] titrated a large number of dicarboxylic acids potentiometrically in pyridine with sodium methoxide and in acetone with tetrabutylammonium hydroxide. Citric acid, $pK_1 = 3.5$, $pK_2 = 4.8$, $pK_3 = 6.4$ (all in water), gives potentiometric breaks when 1 and 3 moles of titrant per mole of acid have been added.

A number of dicarboxylic acids have also been titrated conducto-metrically in dimethylformamide-benzene and other solvents with tetra-butylammonium hydroxide.[5] Most of the acid titrated gave "N-shape" curves.

Carboxylic Acid Anhydrides and Chlorides

Acid anhydrides and chlorides are not primary acids and do not react instantaneously with bases. In fact, they do not react at all with tertiary amines under anhydrous conditions. However, acid anhydrides and chlorides do react with primary and secondary amines; and this is the basis for most procedures for their determination. Johnson and Funk[6] developed a method in which carboxylic-acid anhydrides react with a standard solution of morpholine in anhydrous methanol. After 5 minutes at room temperature the excess morpholine is titrated with methanolic hydrochloric acid to a visual end point using methyl yellow-methylene blue mixed indicator.

$$(RCO)_2O \ + \ HN\!\!\bigcirc\!\!O \ \longrightarrow \ RCON\!\!\bigcirc\!\!O \ + \ RCO_2H$$

$$HCl \ + \ HN\!\!\bigcirc\!\!O \ \longrightarrow \ \left[H_2N\!\!\bigcirc\!\!O\right]^+ \ Cl^-$$

Carboxylic acids weaker than $pK_a \sim 2.3$ do not interfere in the determination of anhydride by this method. Phthalic[7] and maleic anhydride,[8] and perhaps other acid anhydrides may be titrated directly with sodium methoxide to form a half-ester.

Carboxylic acid chlorides may also be determined by reaction with sodium methoxide or with an amine. In the method of Lohr[9] acid chlorides are determined by direct potentiometric titration with cyclo-hexylamine in tetrahydrofurane, using glass and calomel electrodes.

A sharp potential break of approximately 300 mv occurs at the end point. However, increments of titrant must be added slowly near the equivalence point; and a complete titration requires about 15 minutes to perform. Small amounts of acid anhydride do not interfere.

Stahl and Siggia[10] determine acid chlorides by reaction with *m*-chloroaniline in acetone.

Then, the *m*-chloroanilinium chloride is titrated potentiometrically with aqueous sodium hydroxide. Any carboxylic acid that is present is also titrated, but the carboxylic acid is weaker than the *m*-chloroanilinium chloride and gives a separate potentiometric break. Thus, mixtures containing both acid chloride and carboxylic acid can be analyzed. Any free hydrochloric acid in the sample is determined by a separate potentiometric titration in ethyl ether-chlorobenzene with tripropylamine in chlorobenzene.

Enols

  1,3-Diketones are known to exist also in an enolic form which is acidic:

$$\underset{RC-CH_2-CR'}{\overset{O\qquad\qquad O}{||\qquad\qquad||}} \leftrightarrow \underset{RC=CH-CR'}{\overset{OH\quad\ O}{|\qquad\ ||}} \rightleftharpoons \underset{RC=CH-CR'}{\overset{O^-\quad\ O}{|\qquad\ ||}} + H^+$$

In general, compounds of the type $A-CH_2-A'$ are sufficiently acidic to permit titration provided A and A' are groups possessing suitable electron-withdrawing properties. If A and A' are any combination of

$$\underset{-C-R,}{\overset{O}{||}} \quad \underset{-C-H,}{\overset{O}{||}} \quad \underset{-C-OR,}{\overset{O}{||}} \quad \underset{-C-NHAr,}{\overset{O}{||}} \quad \text{or} \quad -C{\equiv}N,$$

accurate titration in dimethylformamide with sodium methoxide is possible using azo violet indicator;[11] or the compound may be titrated potentiometrically in acetone with tetrabutylammonium hydroxide.[12] The amide group has weaker electron-withdrawing properties as shown by the fact that cyanoacetamide is a much weaker acid than compounds containing the other groups, and malonamide is too weakly acidic to be titrated at all.

  Substitution of the methylene group weakens the acidity of an enol. Zaugg and Garven[13] titrated malonic esters in the presence of mono-substituted esters, $EtO_2C-\underset{\overset{|}{R}}{CH}-CO_2Et$, in dimethylformamide using

potassium methoxide titrant and azo violet indicator. Monosubstituted malonate esters may be titrated alone or in the presence of disubstituted esters in ethylenediamine solvent using *o*-nitroaniline indicator.

Imides

  Compounds having the configuration $A-NH-A'$ may be titrated as acids if A and A' are any combination of the following electron-withdrawing groups:

$$\underset{-C-R,}{\overset{O}{||}} \quad \underset{-C-H,}{\overset{O}{||}} \quad \underset{-C-OR,}{\overset{O}{||}} \quad \text{or} \quad \underset{-C-NHAr}{\overset{O}{||}}$$

If either of the electron-withdrawing groups is $\underset{-C-NH_2}{\overset{O}{||}}$ or $\underset{-C-NHR}{\overset{O}{||}}$, a straight-chain imide is quite weakly acidic; however, a cyclic compound such as a hydantoin is easily titratable:

$$R-\underset{\underset{\underset{O}{\parallel}}{\underset{}{C}}}{\overset{\overset{R'}{|}}{C}}-\underset{NH}{\overset{}{\underset{}{}}}C=O$$

hydantoin

Imides have been titrated in dimethylformamide with sodium methoxide (azo-violet indicator)[11] and in acetone with tetrabutylammonium hydroxide.[12]

A 1,2-dicarbonyl group has greater electron-withdrawing ability than a single carbonyl group. Thus, oxanilide, $C_6H_5NHCOCONHC_6H_5$, may be titrated as a monoprotic acid in dimethylformamide; but diphenylurea $C_6H_5NHCONHC_6H_5$, displays no pronounced acidic properties. Oxamide, $NH_2COCONH_2$, cannot be titrated as an acid. Therefore, the aryl groups in oxanilide apparently have an appreciable electron-withdrawing effect.

Inorganic Acids

In most instances, it is best to titrate strong mineral acids in aqueous solution rather than nonaqueous solution. In fact, strong acids may react partially with acetone, 2-propanol, dimethylformamide, acetonitrile, and other solvents, resulting in a non-stoichiometric titration.[14] However, titration of strong inorganic acids is satisfactory in pyridine,[14] t-butyl alcohol,[15] and in organic solvents containing several percent of water.

Titration in a nonaqueous solvent is advantageous for the resolution of a mixture of a strong acid and a weaker acid. For example, sulfuric acid, which acts as a strong diprotic acid in water, gives a sharp potentiometric break for titration of each of its two hydrogens in t-butyl alcohol (see Fig. 7.2). This figure also shows that increasing amounts of water mixed with the t-butyl alcohol increase the magnitude of the first break at the expense of the second. Mixtures of sulfuric and another strong acid may be analyzed by titration in t-butyl alcohol,[15] pyridine,[14] or acetone containing some water.[16] The strong acid plus the first hydrogen of the sulfuric acid are titrated at the first end point. The difference between the first and second end points represents the titration of the second hydrogen of the sulfuric acid.

Mixtures containing phosphoric acid have also been analyzed by titration in pyridine with tetrabutylammonium hydroxide.[17] Mixtures containing sulfuric and hydrochloric acids have been resolved by conductometric titration with lithium acetate.[18]

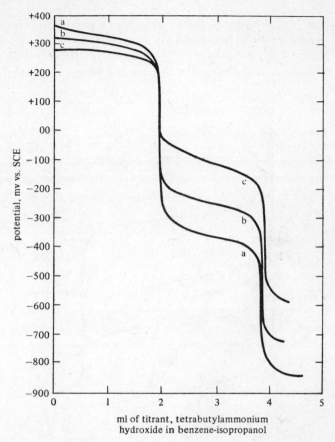

Figure 7.2 *Effect of water on titration of sulfuric acid in t-butyl alcohol with tetrabutylammonium hydroxide: (a) 0.00% H_2O, (b) 0.9% H_2O, (c) 4.4% H_2O. [Reprinted from J. S. Fritz and L. W. Marple,* Anal. Chem., **34** *(1962): 921. Copyright 1962 by the American Chemical Society. Reprinted by permission of the copyright owner.]*

Nitro Compounds

  Several types of aromatic nitro compounds can be titrated quantitatively as acids in pyridine[19] and probably in other solvents as well. Nitro derivatives of aniline and diphenylamine are acidic provided the nitro group, which has powerful electron-withdrawing properties, is in the *ortho* or *para* position with regard to the amine group. One or more halogens in the ring also increases the acidity through an inductive effect, although the effect is less than a nitro group. The minimum structural requirements for titration of aniline derivatives are two nitro groups in *ortho* or *para* positions, or one nitro and two chloro or bromo groups in these positions. Diphenylamine derivatives may be titrated if there is a nitro group either ortho or para to the amine. 4-Nitrodiphenylamine

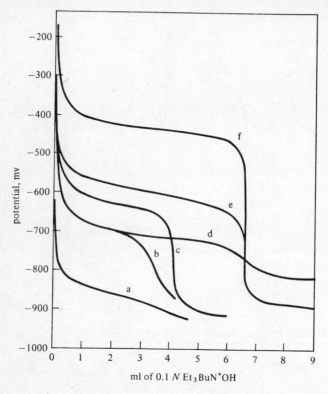

Figure 7.3 *Titration of nitroaniline derivatives in pyridine: (a) 2-nitroaniline, (b) 2-nitro-4-chloroaniline, (c) 2,6-dichloro-4-nitroaniline, (d) 2-chloro-4-nitroaniline, (e) 2,4-dinitroaniline, (f) 2,4,6-trinitroaniline (picramide). [Reprinted from J. S. Fritz, A. J. Moye, and M. Johnson Richard, Anal. Chem., 29 (1957): 1685. Copyright 1957 by the American Chemical Society. Reprinted by permission of the copyright owner.]*

is a considerably stronger acid than 2-nitrodiphenylamine. Titration curves for several nitro aromatic amines are illustrated in Fig. 7.3.

Polynitroaromatic compounds may also be titrated as acids in pyridine[19] with a quaternary ammonium hydroxide. When the benzene ring contains two nitro groups (as in 2,4-dinitrotoluene), the titration is marginal; when three nitro groups are present (as in 1,3,5-trinitrobenzene or in 2,4,6-trinitrotoluene), the results are very good. This titration involves addition of −OH or −OR from the titrant to the benzene ring and requires a slightly slower rate of titration than a simple acid–base titration. The titration of 2,4-dinitrophenylhydrazone derivatives of aldehydes or ketones[20] and 3,5-dinitrobenzoate esters of alcohols[21] are useful applications of this method.

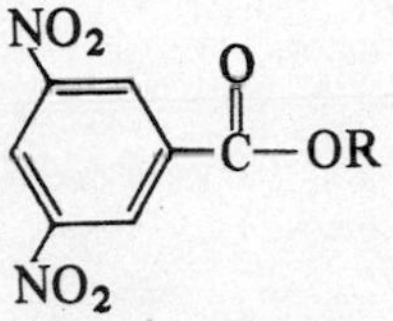

3,5-dinitrobenzoate ester 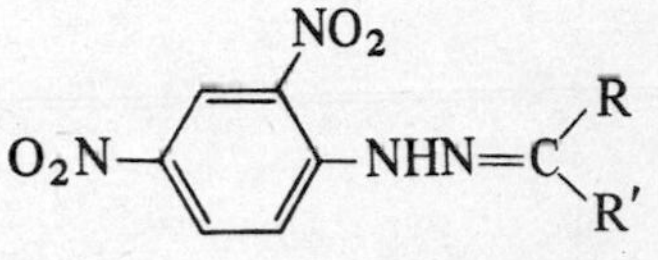   2,4-dinitrophenylhydrazone

Smith and Haglund[22] titrated these and dinitro derivatives of thiols and amines as acids in acetone or pyridine.

Nitromethane has been titrated as an acid in pyridine and other solvents. The acidity of nitroalkanes is usually explained on the basis of an acidic *aci* form.

aci

However, van der Heijde and Dahmen believe that the normal form is titrated because the titration proceeds instantaneously and shows no homoconjugation effects.[23]

Phenols

Unsubstituted and alkyl substituted phenols are weakly acidic and cannot be titrated readily in water or in most alcohols. Historically, Moss, Elliott, and Hall[24] scored a breakthrough by titrating weakly acidic phenols in anhydrous ethylenediamine solution. They employed sodium aminoethoxide·in ethanolamine-ethylenediamine as a titrant and monitored the titration potentiometrically. Later it was shown that phenolic esters of carboxylic acids can also be titrated under similar conditions.[25] Apparently these esters undergo aminolysis with the solvent.

$$RCO_2Ar + NH_2CH_2CH_2NH_2 \rightarrow RCO_2NHCH_2CH_2NH_2 + ArOH$$

The liberated phenol is then titrated as an acid.

Ethylenediamine is a leveling solvent for most acids, and phenols are usually best titrated in a less acidic solvent such as *t*-butyl alcohol,[15,26] pyridine,[27] acetone,[12] methyl ethyl ketone or acetonitrile using a quaternary ammonium hydroxide titrant. Curves for titration of some phenols in acetone are shown in Fig. 7.4.

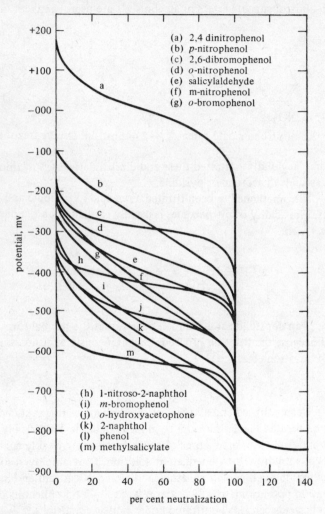

Figure 7.4 *Titration of phenols in acetone with triethyl-n-butylammonium hydroxide. [Reprinted from J. S. Fritz and S. S. Yamamura,* Anal. Chem., **29** *(1957): 1079. Copyright 1957 by the American Chemical Society. Reprinted by permission of the copyright owner.]*

Actually not all phenols are weak acids. Substitution of electron-withdrawing groups in the benzene ring increase the acidity significantly, especially, if the groups are *ortho* or *para* to the phenolic group. From the curves in Fig. 7.4 it is found that the electron-withdrawing groups increase the acidity of phenols in the order: $-NO_2 > -CHO > COR > -Cl$, $-Br > -C_6H_5$. Alkyl groups decrease the acidity somewhat.

The slope of some of the curves in Fig. 7.4 from about 10% to 90% titration is unusually steep. On the other hand, the titration curves for a few compounds are very flat in this region. This has been explained by Van der Heijde.[28] The steep slopes are caused by association of one molecule of phenol with one molecule of phenolate anion. This

structure is sufficiently stable that the bonded hydrogen is more difficult to neutralize than the hydrogen from a phenol monomer. Thus, between two molecules of phenol one hydrogen is more acidic and the other is less acidic than usual. This causes the observed steepness in the titration curve. Similar behavior is observed in the titration of carboxylic acids.

The flat curve of 2,6-dibromophenol (see Fig. 7.4) is explained by steric hindrance preventing dimerization. The flat slope of the methyl salicylate curve is caused by intramolecular association which occurs instead of association between two molecules of phenol.

Dimerization is enhanced by a solvent of low basicity and low solvating power. Added proof is supplied by Bruss and Harlow,[29] who performed conductometric titrations in toluene and other hydrocarbon solvents. The conductometric curves have two inflections: The first where one-half mole of tetrabutylammonium hydroxide titrant per mole of phenol has been added, and the second when one mole of titrant has been added. The dimerization of 2,6-disubstituted phenols is hindered sterically, and no conductometric inflection is obtained.

The steep potentiometric curves of phenols and carboxylic acids have a very detrimental effect on the differentiating titration of two or more acids of different strength. An amphiprotic solvent such as an alcohol will prevent dimerization and give a flatter curve. Unfortunately most alcohols are too acidic for the titration of very weak acids. However, t-butyl alcohol can be used as a solvent for the titration of weak acids. Because of its amphiprotic nature, dimerization of phenols and carboxylic acids is prevented and titration curves are flat. Because of this, t-butyl alcohol is recommended as a solvent for the differentiating titration of mixtures of phenols.

Hummelstedt and Hume[30] give recommended wavelengths for spectrophotometric titration of 16 different phenols in 2-propanol. In a few cases, they were able to analyze mixtures of closely related phenols. For example, a mixture containing *para*- and *meta*-nitrophenol (pK_a in H_2O = 7.1 and 8.3, respectively) was successfully resolved.

Phenols with alkyl substituents in the aromatic ring are quite weakly acidic and do not give a very sharp end point, even in nonaqueous solvents. Marple and Fritz[31] found that the addition of tetrabutyl-ammonium bromide at the start of a titration enhances the sharpness of the potentiometric break when alkyl-substituted phenols are titrated in t-butyl alcohol. The tetrabutylammonium phenolate formed in the titration reaction exists partly as the ion pair and partly as free ions. The higher concentration (0.2–0.3 M) of the more highly dissociated tetrabutyl-ammonium bromide represses the dissociation of the phenolate and thus makes the titration equilibrium more favorable.

$$Bu_4N^+OH^- + ArOH \rightleftharpoons H_2O + Bu_4N^+OAr^- \rightleftharpoons Bu_4N^+ + OAr^-$$

$$Bu_4N^+ \text{ (from } Bu_4N^+Br^-) + OAr^- \rightleftharpoons Bu_4N^+OAr^-$$

Salts

Salts of the type $B \cdot HA$ can be titrated provided the salt can be dissolved and if the basic constituent, B, is not too strongly basic and the acid HA, is not too weakly acidic. Most ammonium and amine salts are titratable as acids in dimethylformamide,[32] ethylenediamine,[32] or dimethylsulfoxide.[33] Salts of carboxylic and mineral acids usually give sharp end points. Guanidine salts give poor end points because of the rather strong base liberated; most quaternary ammonium salts cannot be titrated as acids.

Salts that are difficultly soluble in the organic solvents listed may be dissolved in a small amount of water and titrated after the addition of ethylenediamine or dimethylsulfoxide. As much as 11% water may be present when amine salts are titrated in dimethylsulfoxide with tetrabutyl-ammonium hydroxide.[33] Water causes high results in DMF, however, probably because of hydrolysis of the solvent to formic acid.

Sulfonamides

Sulfonamides of the type $ArSO_2NH-$ can be titrated as acids in common solvents. The sulfonamides of aromatic amines are more acidic than those of aliphatic amines, but both can be titrated. The nonaqueous titration of 21 sulfonamides with sodium methoxide has been reported.[34] Differentiating titrations of sulfathiazole-sulfapyridine and sulfathiazole-sulfanilamide with tetrabutvlammonium hydroxide also are possible.[12]

Sulfonic Acids

These strong acids are titratable under a variety of conditions. Many are water soluble and can be determined by titration with aqueous sodium hydroxide. However, water is a leveling solvent for strong acids, and titration in a nonaqueous solvent is advantageous for distinguishing between sulfonic acids and other strong or intermediate strength acids. Mixtures of sulfonic and sulfuric acids may be resolved by titration in a nonaqueous solvent where the sulfuric acid gives two potentiometric breaks (see p. 100). Pietrzyk and Belisle[35] found that methyl isobutyl ketone is a good solvent for distinguishing between aromatic sulfonic acids with various other substituents in the ring. Benzenesulfonic acid and the mono-, di, and trinitro derivatives may be distinguished by titration in acetic anhydride with pyridine.[36]

Sodium sulfonate may be assayed by first passing an aqueous solution of the sample through a cation-exchange column to convert salts to the acids. The sample is washed through the column with acetone, diluted with more acetone, and the acids titrated.[37] If any sulfuric acid is present at this point, the potentiometric titration curve will show a second break. The difference between the two breaks represents the base needed to titrate the second hydrogen of sulfuric acid.

Miscellaneous Acids

Thiophenols are more acidic than the corresponding phenols and are readily titratable as acids. Aliphatic thiols (mercaptans) are much less acidic and alkalimetric determination is less attractive than other analytical

methods which are available. Diphenylthiourea, $C_6H_5NH\overset{\overset{\displaystyle S}{\|}}{C}NHC_6H_5$, may be titrated as a monobasic acid in DMF.[11] Sulfinic acids may be titrated in *t*-butyl alcohol, DMF or DMSO.[38] The instability of sulfinic acids necessitates careful handling to avoid autooxidation.

Phosphinic acids, $R_2\overset{\overset{\displaystyle O}{\|}}{P}-OH$, are fairly strong and may be titrated without difficulty in solvents such as methanol, DMF, DMSO, and pyridine.[39]

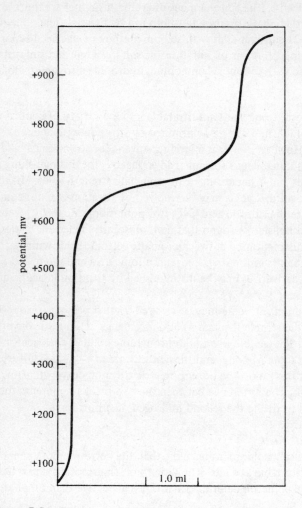

Figure 7.5 *Titration of hydriotic acid-n-butyl iodide mixture in pyridine with tetrabutylammonium hydroxide. [Reprinted from R. H. Cundiff and P. C. Markunas,* Anal. Chem., **33** *(1961): 1028. Copyright 1961 by the American Chemical Society. Reprinted by permission of the copyright owner.]*

Little has been done with phosphonic acids, $R_3\overset{\displaystyle O}{\overset{\|}{P}}(OH)_2$, but the acid dissociation constants in water, $pK_1 = 2$ to 3, $pK_2 = 7$ to 8, suggest that two good breaks should be obtainable.

Hydroxamic acids, $R\overset{\displaystyle NH}{\overset{\|}{C}}{-}OH$, have been titrated quantitatively in dimethylformamide with tetrabutylammonium hydroxide.[40]

Acidimetric titration is a good way to measure carbon dioxide. In one method, carbon dioxide is absorbed in dry acetone containing 0.5% methanol; and the carbon dioxide is titrated coulometrically to thymol-blue end point.[41]

An alkalimetric determination of alkyl iodides is quite useful as part of an analytical method for determining alkoxyl groups.[42] In this method alkoxides are cleaved with hydriodic acid.

$$-OR + HI \rightarrow -OH + RI,$$

where $R = C_1$ to C_4. The alkyl iodide is distilled into pyridine, where it reacts to form an alkyl pyridinium iodide, $(C_5H_5\overset{\cdot}{N}{-}R)^+I^-$, which can be titrated as a weak acid. Some hydrogen iodide also distills over and is titrated. The difference between the first and second end points (see Fig. 7.5) represents the alkyl pyridinium iodide, which is equivalent to the alkoxyl group in the original sample.

7.2 Coulometric Titration of Acids

A disadvantage of a quaternary ammonium hydroxide for the titration of acids is the difficulty of preparing it free from impurities. A method is available for preparing pure titrant,[43] but it is a rather long and involved process. Dilute solutions of base especially must be handled very carefully to avoid contamination with carbonate impurities, and the titrant solutions slowly decompose on standing to form small amounts of tertiary amines.

Coulometric generation of base should avoid these difficulties because the titrant is generated at the time an acid is being titrated. There is no physical transfer of a basic titrant from one container to another. Streuli *et al.*[44] showed that acids of moderate strength may be titrated coulometrically in acetone with a quaternary ammonium halide as the electrolyte for generation of the base. Williams and his students[45] generated a quaternary ammonium hydroxide coulometrically in benzene-methanol and in *t*-butyl alcohol–methanol. Fritz and Gainer[46] developed an improved system for coulometric titration in *t*-butyl alcohol that is applicable to the titration of weak acids as well as stronger acids. Their system is as follows:

Cathode Compartment

A platinum electrode of large area is used. The cathode compartment is filled with $0.1M$ tetrabutylammonium bromide in *t*-butyl alcohol. Since *t*-butyl alcohol contains approximately 0.2% water (Karl Fischer titration), the probable electrode reaction is

$$H_2O + e^- \rightarrow OH^- + 1/2H_2(g)$$

Anode Compartment

A platinum electrode is used because difficulty was encountered with the silver halide coating that forms on a silver electrode. The compartment is filled with $0.1M$ tetramethylammonium bromide in methanol, which has a lower electrical resistance than *t*-butyl alcohol. The electrode reaction is

$$Br^- \rightarrow 1/2Br_2 + e^-$$

Compartment Divider

An anion-exchange membrane is used to separate the anode and cathode compartments. (In some cases, a cation-exchange membrane was placed behind the anion-exchange membrane on the anode side; but this appears to be unnecessary.) The membrane used offers lower electrical resistance than does a glass frit. Also, hydrostatic pressure does not force the anode liquid through the anion-exchange membrane as it does with a glass frit.

Indicator Titrations

The titration cell contains a Teflon anode compartment with electrodes for both the anode and cathode compartments mounted in it (Fig. 7.6). This fits into a simple, low-cost glass container (a cut-off beaker) that can easily be washed or replaced. Each compartment is filled with approximately 35 ml of electrolyte solution. A suitable indicator for a particular titration is selected from the transition ranges in *t*-butyl alcohol (Fig. 5.5) after the end-point potential has been ascertained by a potentiometric titration of the acid in question.

Potentiometric Titrations

The titration cell used is shown in Fig. 7.7. The nonaqueous salt bridge to the calomel reference electrode is of a type used by Marple and

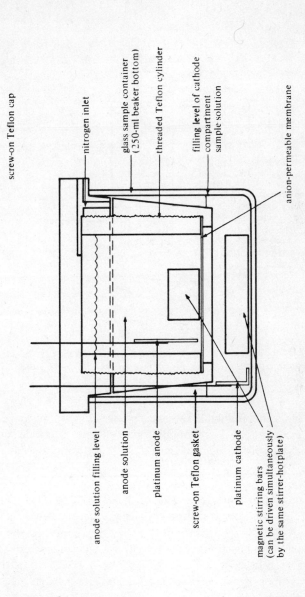

Figure 7.6 *Cell for coulometric titration of acids using indicators (as designed by M. D. Seymour).*

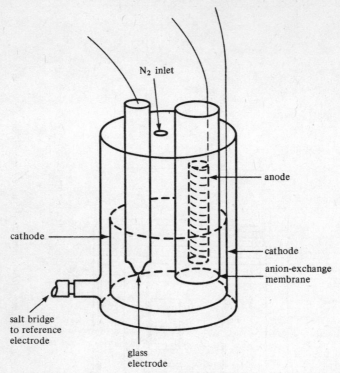

Figure 7.7 *Coulometric titration assembly for potentiometric end points in t-butyl alcohol. [Reprinted from J. S. Fritz and F. E. Gainer, Talanta, 15 (1968): 939.*

Fritz[43] and gives a reproducible reference potential. An all-purpose glass indicator electrode is used. A combination glass-calomel electrode is convenient when the absolute values of the potentials are not important.

Current Supply

Constant current for generation of the basic titrant is supplied by a commerical coulometric current source. The applicable current rates are 5 mA to 50 mA for indicator titrations and 5 mA to 20 mA for potentiometric titrations. With higher currents the cell resistance increases and the current efficiency is lowered. The crux of the problem seems to be the difficulty in transporting ions at a sufficiently fast rate through the ion-exchange membrane.

To test the current efficiency, a large number of samples of primary standard benzoic acid were titrated in *t*-butyl alcohol, with

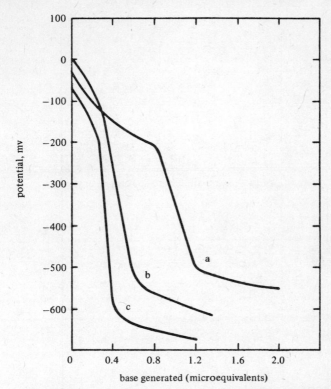

Figure 7.8   *Titration of t-butyl alcohol solvent blanks with electrically generated titrant: (a) undistilled solvent, (b) single distilled solvent, (c) double distilled solvent. [Reprinted from J. S. Fritz and F. E. Gainer, Talanta, 15 (1968): 939.*

2,4-dinitrodiphenylamine being used as visual indicator. Results for 20-60 μ equiv samples showed a current efficiency of 100.0 ± 0.5%. Therefore, 100.0% current efficiency was assumed in all subsequent titrations. Results for some 354 titrations of different acids with visual indicators are summarized in Table 7.1.

Excellent potentiometric titration curves were obtained, but it was not possible to record titration curves while the titrant was being generated. Titration curves have to be plotted manually by generating an increment of titrant and then shutting off the coulometer while the potential is measured.

For the accurate titration of strong acids, it is necessary to use very pure tetrabutylammonium bromide, to purify the solvent and to substract the bulk which remains despite these precautions. The curves in Fig. 7.8 show that the solvent blank may be reduced appreciably by

TABLE 7.1

Coulometric Titrations in Butyl Alchol

Compounds titrated	No. of samples	Amount taken, μequiv	Recovery, %	Std. deviation, %	Indicator
Benzoic acid	59	10–60	100.1₅	0.17	2,4-dinitroaniline
Phenol	96	12–61	100.1	0.21	2-nitroaniline
2,4,6-Trimethylphenol	7	20	99.7₅	0.41	2-nitroaniline
2-Hydroxyphenol	6	20	99.4	0.19	Azo Violet
Anthranilic acid	41	10–60	100.1	0.13	2,4-dinitroaniline
Succinic acid (1st H)	13	10–20	99.7	0.08	Bromothymol Blue
(2nd H)	17	10–60	99.4	0.13	Azo Violet
Acetoacetanilide	10	20	99.8₅	0.12	Azo Violet
Dibenzoylmethane	22	20–48	99.9	0.11	Azo Violet
Succinimide	25	10–60	99.9	0.22	Azo Violet
Hydrantoin	16	20	99.5	0.11	Azo Violet
2-Cyanoacetamide	12	20	99.7	0.15	p-nitro-p'-aminoazobenzene
Ethyl cyanoacetate	10	20	99.1	0.07	Azo Violet
2,4-Pentanedione	8	30	97.5	0.06	Azo Violet
p-Toluenesulphonic acid	12	20–60	99.9	0.08	Bromothymol Blue

double distillation of the *t*-butyl alcohol. Purification also largely avoids the buffering effect of weak acid impurities on the titration of strong acids such as sulfuric or aromatic sulfonic acids.

7.3   Analysis of Mixtures

A differentiating titration of two or more acids in a mixture is often possible. The solvent used should permit titration of weak acids but not be so basic that stronger acids are leveled. It is best to use a good solvating solvent so that homoconjugation will not cause the titration curve to have an abnormally steep slope in the buffer region and make it more difficult to obtain separate potentiometric breaks for acids of different strength.

The feasibility of performing a differentiating titration of a mixture of acids is predictable from the titration curves of the individual acids. If the slopes of the titration curves are fairly flat in the buffer region and if the difference be at least from 100 to 200 mv in the half-neutralization potentials, it should be possible to resolve the mixture. This is illustrated by Fig. 7.9, which shows curves for titration of individual phenols in *t*-butyl alcohol, and by Fig. 7.10, which shows separate breaks for a mixture of four of these phenols.

Mixtures containing acids of different types may also be resolved providing the compounds are of sufficiently different acid strength and do not react chemically with each other in solution. Examples of these would be mixtures of carboxylic acids.

7.4   Titration of Very Weak Acids

Alcohols and other extremely weakly acidic compounds can be titrated quantitatively as acids in an appropriate nonaqueous solvent base. Conditions must be strictly anhydrous because water is about the same order of acidity as some of the compounds to be titrated as acids. In some cases oxygen must also be excluded because the strongly basic titrants are also reducing agents and may be oxidized by oxygen.

Higuchi, Concha and Kuramoto[47] titrated alcohols as acids in tetrahydrofurane with a solution of lithium aluminum amide, $(R_2N)_4LiAl$, in the same solvent as the titrant. The titrant is prepared by reacting lithium aluminum hydride with a secondary amine such as

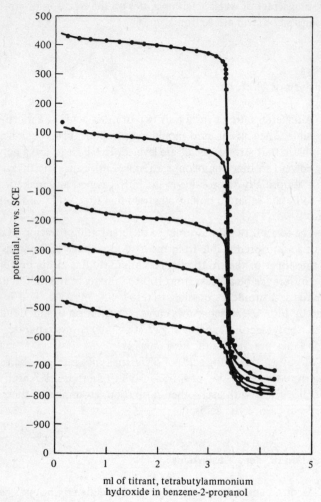

Figure 7.9 *Titration of nitrophenols in* t-*butyl alcohol with tetrabutylammonium hydroxide:* □ *picric acid,* ○ *2,4-dinitro-phenol,* △p-*nitrophenol,* ▽m-*nitrophenol,* ● *phenol [Reprinted from J. S. Fritz and L. W. Marple,* Anal. Chem., **34** *(1962): 921. Copyright 1962 by the American Chemical Society. Reprinted by permission of the copyright owner.]*

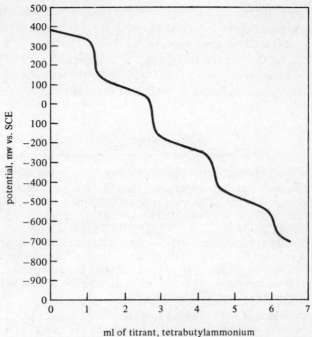

Figure 7.10 *Differentiating titration of picric acid; 2,4-dinitrophenol, 2-nitrophenol, and phenol in t-butyl alcohol. [Reprinted from J. S. Fritz and L. W. Marple, Anal. Chem., 34 (1962): 921. Copyright 1962 by the American Chemical Society. Reprinted by permission of the copyright owner.]*

dibutylamine, or piperidine. Titrations are performed under nitrogen using p-phenylaminoazobenzene as a visual indicator. Silanols[48] and ethanolamine[49] have been titrated as acids in dimethoxymethane using a similar procedure.

Sodium triphenylmethane, $(C_6H_5)_3C^-Na^+$, and sodium dimethylsulfoxide, $Na^+(CH_2SOCH_3)^-$, have been used for titration of extremely weak acids. Of these, the latter is the most promising. Price and Whiting[50] used sodium dimethylsulfoxide and DMSO solvent to titrate water, phenols, alcohols, nitromethane, amides, thiols, diphenylamide, purrole, phenylacetylene, cyclopentadiene, and indene. The end point of a titration is indicated by a small amount of added triphenylmethane, which turns red when the first permanent excess of base is added:

$$Na^+(CH_2SOCH_3)^- + (C_6H_5)_3CH \rightarrow (C_6H_5)_3C^-Na^+ + CH_3SOCH_3$$

117

Titrations are performed in a closed container flushed with nitrogen, and all reagents are introduced by means of a syringe. A 1-M solution of the titrant in DMSO is added from a special "anaerobic" buret.

Courtot-Coupez and Le Démézet[51] measured the dissociation constants of some very weak acids in DMSO potentiometrically using sodium mimethylsulfoxide to convert half of the acid to its salt.

PROBLEMS

1. (a) From the following data construct a titration curve for acidic impurities in a nonaqueous solvent. First is given ml. 0.10 M Bu$_4$NOH, then potential in mv: 0.00 ml, +100 mv; 0.02 ml, 0.00 mv; 0.03 ml, −110 mv; 0.04 ml, −205 mv; 0.05 ml, −285 mv; 0.06 ml, −500 mv; 0.07 ml, −720 mv; 0.08 ml, −750 mv; 0.10 ml, −800 mv.
   (b) Titration of a mixture of two acids in this same solvent produces an end point at 3.54 ml (−150 mv) and a second end point at a buret reading of 9.05 ml (−400 mv). Subtract the appropriate solvent blanks from the curve in part (a) and calculate the correct volume of titrant to titrate each of the two acids.

2. Indicate which of the following compounds are acidic enough to be titrated with tetrabutylammonium hydroxide in an appropriate solvent.

(a) $CH_3-\overset{\displaystyle CO_2Et}{\underset{\displaystyle CO_2Et}{CH}}$

(b) $\overset{\displaystyle CH_2-CO_2Et}{\underset{\displaystyle CH_2-CO_2Et}{|}}$

(c) $\overset{\displaystyle CONH_2}{\underset{\displaystyle CONH_2}{CH_2}}$

(d) $\overset{\displaystyle CO_2Na}{\underset{\displaystyle C\equiv N}{CH_2}}$

(e) $\overset{\displaystyle CH_2-CO}{\underset{\displaystyle CH_2-CO}{|}} NH$

(f) (benzene ring with CH$_3$, OH, CH$_3$ substituents)

(g) C$_6$H$_5$—OCOCH$_3$

(h) C$_6$H$_5$—CH$_2$OH

(i) $C_6H_5SO_2NR_2$

(j) $C_6H_5NHCSNHC_6H_5$

3. Explain how an acid–base titration could be used to follow the progress of each of the following chemical reactions with respect to reaction time:

(a) O_2N-⟨benzene with NO_2⟩$-Cl$ + 2 ⟨benzene⟩$-NH_2$ $\longrightarrow$

O_2N-⟨benzene with NO_2⟩$-NH-$⟨benzene⟩ + ⟨benzene⟩$-\overset{+}{N}H_3Cl^-$

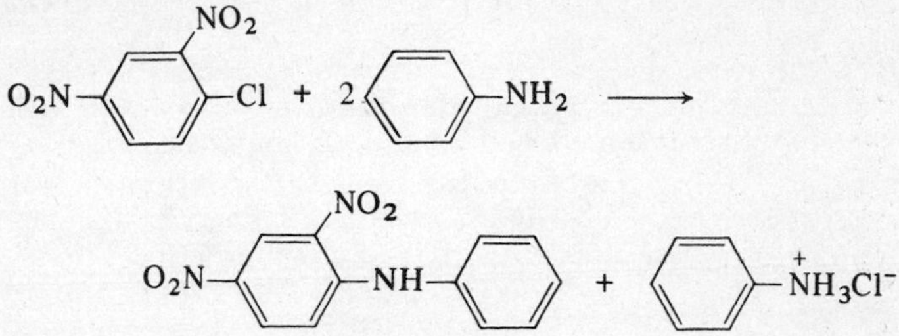

(b) CH_3-⟨benzene⟩ + H_2SO_4 $\longrightarrow$

CH_3-⟨benzene⟩$-SO_3H$ + H_2O

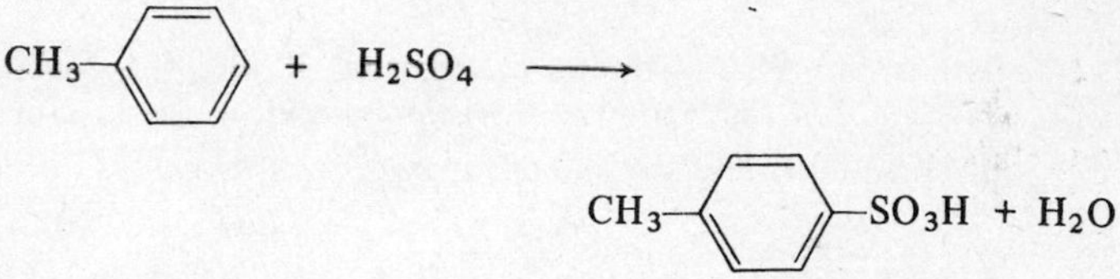

4. (a) Write a chemical equation illustrating homoconjugation during titration of a carboxylic acid in a nonaqueous solvent.
(b) In what type of solvent does homoconjugation occur?
(c) How does homoconjugation affect the potentiometric titration curve of a carboxylic acid?
(d) How may homoconjugation be prevented?

5. Outline a scheme for analysis of each of the following mixtures by acid–base titration. Give the titrant, solvent, and any other essential conditions.

(a)   ⟨benzene⟩$-SO_3H$, O_2N-⟨benzene⟩$-SO_3H$

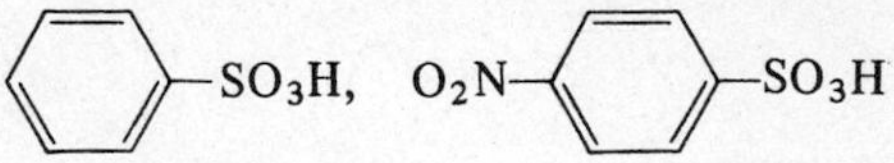

(b)   ⟨benzene⟩ with CO_2H and OH ,   ⟨benzene⟩ with CO_2H and HO

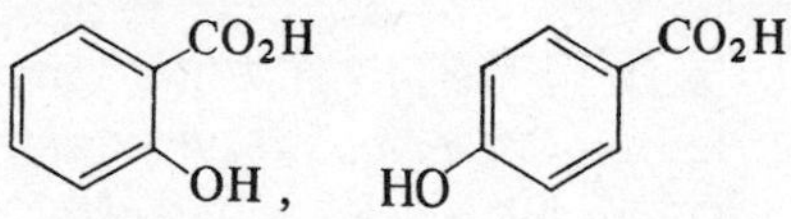

(c) $(C_4H_9)_4N^+Cl^-$, $(C_4H_9)_3NH^+Cl^-$

(d) $(RCO)_2O$, RCO_2H

(e) C_4H_9-⟨benzene⟩$-OH$ C_3H_8CO-⟨benzene⟩$-OH$

119

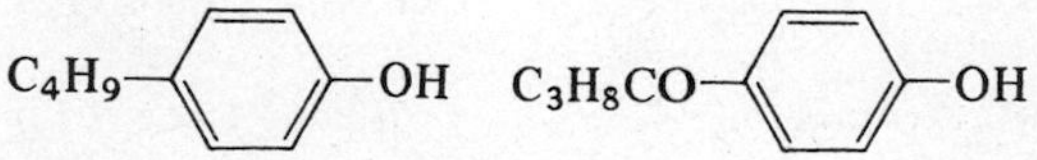

6. A coulometric titration is performed as described in Chap. 7, but the cathode compartment is filled with 0.1 M tetramethylammonium bromide in 2-propanol containing some water.
    (a) Write equations for the electrochemical reactions which occur at each electrode.
    (b) What advantages and disadvantages would you expect from the solution used in the cathode compartment compared with a solution of tetrabutylammonium bromide in t-butyl alcohol?

7. An acid having an equivalent weight of 84 is titrated coulometrically at 10.0 mA. Calculate the weight of this acid in milligrams that can be titrated in 5.00 min at 100% current efficiency.

REFERENCES

1. G. Kortum, W. Vogel, and K. Andrussow, *Dissociation Constants of Organic Acids in Aqueous Solution*, London: Butterworths, 1961.

2. R. H. Cundiff and P. C. Markunas, *Anal. Chem.*, **28** (1956), 792.

3. G. A. Harlow and G. E. A. Wyld, *Anal. Chem.*, **30** (1958), 69.

4. T. Jasinski and H. Smagowski, *Chem. Anal. (Warsaw)*, **10** (1965), 1321.

5. N. Van Meurs and E. A. M. F. Dahmen, *Anal. Chim. Acta*, **19** (1958), 64; *Ibid.*, **21** (1959), 10, 443.

6. J. B. Johnson and G. L. Funk, *Anal. Chem.*, **27** (1955), 1464.

7. J. S. Fritz and N. M. Lisicki, *Anal. Chem.*, **23** (1951), 589.

8. H. Huhn and E. Jenckel, *Z. anal. Chem.*, **163** (1958), 427.

9. L. J. Lohr, *Anal. Chem.*, **32** (1960), 1166.

10. C. R. Stahl and S. Siggia, *Anal. Chem.*, **28** (1956), 1971.

11. J. S. Fritz, *Anal. Chem.*, **24** (1952), 674.

12. J. S. Fritz and S. S. Yamamura, *Anal. Chem.*, **29** (1957), 1079.

13. H. E. Zaugg and F. C. Garven, *Anal. Chem.*, **30** (1958), 1444.

14. R. H. Cundiff and P. C. Markunas, *Anal. Chem.*, **30** (1958), 1447.

15. J. S. Fritz and L. W. Marple, *Anal. Chem.*, **34** (1962), 921.

16. H. V. Malmstadt and D. A. Vasallo, *Anal. Chem.*, **31** (1959), 206.

17. R. H. Cundiff and P. C. Markunas, *Anal. Chim. Acta*, **20** (1959), 506.

18. T. Higuchi and C. R. Rehm, *Anal. Chem.*, **27** (1955), 408.

19. J. S. Fritz, A. J. Moye, and M. Johnson Richard, *Anal Chem.*, **29** (1957), 1685.

20. A. J. Sensabaugh, R. H. Cundiff, and P. C. Markunas, *Anal. Chem.*, **30** (1958), 1445.

21. W. T. Robinson, R. H. Cundiff, A. J. Sensabaugh, and P. C. Markunas, *Talanta*, **3** (1960), 307.

22. B. Smith and A. Haglund, *Acta Chem. Scand.*, **15** (1961), 675.

23. H. B. van der Heijde and E. A. M. F. Dahmen, *Anal. Chim. Acta,* **16** (1957), 378.

24. M. L. Moss, J. H. Elliott, and R. T. Hall, *Anal. Chem.*, **20** (1948), 784.

25. R. A. Glenn and J. T. Peaks, *Anal. Chem.*, **27** (1955), 205.

26. N. T. Crabb and F. E. Critchfield, *Talanta*, **10** (1963), 271.

27. C. A. Streuli, *Anal. Chem.*, **32** (1960), 407.

28. H. B. Van der Heijde, *Anal. Chim. Acta*, **16** (1957), 392.

29. D. B. Bruss and G. A. Harlow, *Anal. Chem.*, **30** (1958), 1835.

30. L. E. I. Hummelstedt and D. N. Hume, *Anal. Chem.*, **32** (1960), 1792.

31. L. W. Marple and J. S. Fritz, *Anal. Chem.*, **35** (1963), 1431.

32. J. S. Fritz, *Anal. Chem.*, **24** (1952), 306.

33. K. K. Barnes and C. K. Mann, *Anal. Chem.*, **36** (1964), 2502.

34. J. S. Fritz and R. T. Keen, *Anal. Chem.*, **24** (1952), 308.

35. D. J. Pietrzyk and J. Belisle, *Anal. Chem.*, **38** (1966), 969.

36. D. J. Pietrzyk, *Anal. Chem.*, **39** (1967), 1367.

37. E. H. Griffin and E. W. Albaugh, *Anal. Chem.*, **38** (1966), 921.

38. D. L. Wetzel and C. E. Meloan, *Anal. Chem.*, **36** (1964), 2474.

39. T. Jasinski and A. Modro, *Chem. Anal.* (*Warsaw*), **10** (1965), 929.

40. T. W. Stamey and R. Christian, *Talanta*, **13** (1966), 144.

41. D. C. White, *Talanta*, **13** (1966), 1303.

42. R. H. Cundiff and P. C. Markunas, *Anal. Chem.*, **33** (1961), 1028.

43. L. W. Marple and J. S. Fritz, *Anal. Chem.*, **34** (1962), 796.

44. C. A. Streuli, J. J. Cincotta, D. L. Maricle, and K. K. Mead, *Anal. Chem.*, **36** (1964), 1371.

45. C. Cotman, W. Schreiner, J. Hickey, and T. Williams, *Talanta*, **12** (1965), 17.

46. J. S. Fritz and F. E. Gainer, *Talanta*, **15** (1968), 939.

47. T. Higuchi, J. Concha, and R. Kuramoto, *Anal. Chem.*, **24** (1952), 685.

48. G. E. Kellum and K. L. Uglum, *Anal. Chem.*, **39** (1967), 1623.

49. L. A. Small, *Analyst*, **84** (1959), 117.

50. G. C. Price and M. C. Whiting, *Chem. & Ind.* (1963), 775.

51. J. Courtot-Coupez and M. Le Démézet, *Bull. Chem. Soc. France* (1969), 1033.

CHAPTER 8

Laboratory Procedures

Most of the procedures given here are for titration of samples from a 10 ml buret with $\sim 0.1M$ titrant. The accuracy is almost as good as that using a standard 50 ml buret, and there is considerable saving in the quantity of organic solvents that must be used. The procedures can easily be adapted for use with larger burets by increasing the sample size and amounts of solvent used according to the following recommendations:

Buret	Sample size meq base or acid	Solvent ml
10 ml	0.3-0.8	15-25[a]
25 ml	1.0-2.0	40-50
50 ml	2.0-4.0	60-80

[a] This is for indicator titrations. For potentiometric titrations use 30-40 ml.

A base usually can be titrated in an ordinary flask or beaker; however, most acids titrated with a strong base titrant require protection from the carbon dioxide in the air. For this a plastic top fitted with holes for the buret tip, with a nitrogen inlet and electrodes (if used), is recommended (see Fig. 8.1). The containers should usually be 100-ml beakers with the top rim and lip cut off.

Although ordinary burets may be used, it is convenient to use an automatic buret for titration of acids with a strongly basic titrant in order to avoid contamination with carbonate during transfer of the titrant to the buret. A tube containing Ascarite (or similar carbon dioxide absorbant) and anhydrous magnesium perchlorate should be attached to the reservoir used for storage of basic titrants. In general, acidic titrants may simply be stored in a stoppered bottle with no special protection.

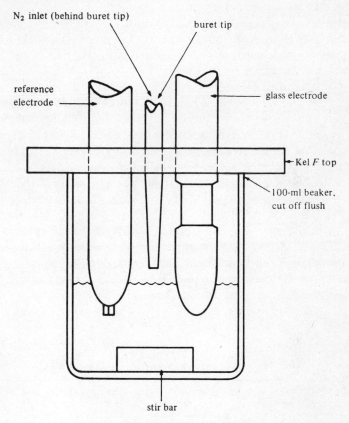

Figure 8.1 *Titration assembly.*

A pH meter, preferably one with provision for scale expansion, is suitable for potentiometric titrations in nonaqueous solvents. Generally, potential readings should be made on the millivolt scale rather than on the pH scale. Other types of direct-reading titrimeters with a high input resistance may also be used. Commercial titrimeters that permit automatic recording of entire potentiometric titration curves are convenient for some applications. Automatic titrimeters that detect a titration end point, especially by potentiometric or colorimetric means, are handy for routine acid–base titrations in nonaqueous solvents.

A general-purpose glass electrode is satisfactory as an indicator electrode. A fiber- or porous-plug type of calomel electrode is a convenient and readily available reference electrode; the porous-plug type gives better electrical contact. For titration of acids, especially, it is best to replace the aqueous potassium choride solution in the calomel electrode with a non-aqueous electrolyte. A saturated solution of tetramethylammonium chloride in 2-propanol is recommended. This solution in the electrode should be renewed every few days.

A modified silver–silver chloride electrode is another satisfactory reference electrode for potentiometric titration of both acids on bases. This may be prepared by electrolyzing a silver wire in chloride solution to coat it with silver chloride, connecting it to an electrical lead, and inserting the wire in the shell of a calomel electrode. The wire is immersed in a saturated solution of tetramethylammonium chloride in 2-propanol.

It is recommended that electrodes be immersed in distilled water for storage. They should be wiped dry with paper tissue just before a titration or series of titrations.

Buchanen[1] found that organic liquids can be accurately measured with glassware that is calibrated for use with aqueous solutions. The volume of pure organic solvent delivered from a 5-ml pipet remained within the stated tolerance of ±2 ppt in every case although a slight low bias was noted. His results are summarized in Table 8.1.

TABLE 8.1
Delivery of Liquids from a 5 ml Pipet

Liquid	Av. vol, ml	Range, ml	Av. diff. from water, ml
Water	5.006	0.004	
Dimethylformamide	5.000	0.005	−0.006
Acetic anhydride	5.005	0.003	−0.005
Acetone	5.000	0.005	−0.006
Benzene	5.006	0.003	−0.006
Acetonitrile	5.002	0.008	−0.004
Acetic acid	4.997	0.003	−0.009
Chloroform	5.000	0.007	−0.006
Nitrobenzene	5.002	0.003	−0.004
Methyl-ethyl ketone	5.007	0.005	+0.001
Ethylenediamine	5.000	0.003	−0.006

SOURCE: E. B. Buchanen, Jr., *Talanta*, 13 (1964), 1599.

The coefficient of cubic expansion of most organic solvents is much larger than water. This means that solutions should be brought to laboratory temperature before they are measured and that laboratory temperature should be kept fairly constant to avoid significant volumetric errors.

8.1 Procedure 1: Preparation and Standardization of Perchloric Acid Titrants

Reagents

0.1 *M* Perchloric acid in glacial acetic acid. Add 8.5 ml of 70-72% perchloric acid to 100-200 ml of ACS grade glacial acetic acid. Add 20 ml of acetic anhydride and allow the solution to stand for about 0.5 h (Note 1). Dilute to 1 liter with glacial acetic acid.

0.1 *M* Perchloric acid in dioxane. Add 8.5 ml of 70-72% perchloric acid to reagent grade 1,4-dioxane and dilute to 1 liter of dioxane (Note 2).

Crystal violet or methyl violet. Dissolve 0.2 g in 100 ml of glacial acetic acid or chlorobenzene.

Procedure

Weigh accurately 100-125 mg samples of primary standard potassium acid phthalate into a small flask and add about 25 ml of glacial acetic acid (Note 3). Heat to boiling to dissolve completely. If any of the solid creeps up the sides of the flask, wash it down with a little acetic acid. Cool, and add 1 or 2 drops of crystal violet or methyl violet indicator, and titrate with 0.1 *M* perchloric acid to a color change of violet to pale blue (not to green or yellow). Calculate the molarity (normality) of the perchloric acid and using 204.2 as the equivalent weight of the potassium acid phthalate.

Notes

1. Acetic anhydride is added to remove most of the water from the titrant:

$$(CH_3CO)_2O + H_2O \rightarrow 2 CH_3CO_2H$$

A satisfactory titrant for most purposes can be prepared without adding any acetic anhydride, but a more anhydrous titrant usually gives a somewhat sharper end point. For titration of very weak bases in solvents containing acetic anhydride, it is recommended that 26 ml of acetic anhydride be added per liter of titrant.

2. Impurities in the dioxane may cause the titrant to darken after a few minutes. This will not affect the usefulness of the titrant unless the solution becomes extremely dark. Titrants made with pure dioxane should not darken appreciably.

3. Proportionately larger samples and solvent should be used if a 25- or 50-ml buret is to be used instead of a 10-ml buret (see p. 122).

8.2   Procedure 2: Titration of Base

Reagents

0.1 *M* Perchloric acid in acetic acid. (See Procedure 1.)

Crystal violet of methyl violet indicator. (See Procedure 1.)

Electrodes

General-purpose glass indicator electrode. Reference electrode may be calomel, modified calomel, or modified silver–silver chloride (see p. 124).

Procedure A: Total Base

Dissolve a sample containing from 0.3 to 0.8 meq of base in 30–40 ml of ACS grade glacial acetic acid (Note 1). Add 1–2 drops of crystal violet indicator; insert a glass indicator electrode and a reference electrode. Titrate potentiometrically with 0.1 *M* perchloric acid in acetic acid. When the indicator changes from violet to blue, green or yellow, note the colors that correspond to the various potential readings.

Plot the titration curves (mv vs. ml of perchloric acid), and ascertain the potential reading and indicator color at the steepest part of the curve. Subsequent titrations of similar samples may be made using this indicator color or potential as the end point (Note 2).

Notes

1. Nitromethane or acetonitrile may be used in place of acetic acid as the solvent. However, a solvent blank should be run to check for basic impurities, and this should not require more than 0.02–0.04 ml of 0.1 *M* perchloric acid for titration.

2. For titrations with a visual indicator the amount of acetic acid used to dissolve the sample can be reduced to 15–25 ml.

Procedure B: Amino Acids

Dissolve a sample containing from 0.3 to 0.8 meq of amino acid in the minimum amount of water possible (usually 1 or 2 drops from a medicine dropper). Add 30–40 ml of glacial acetic acid, and immediately titrate with 0.1 M perchloric acid in acetic acid, according to Procedure 2A.

8.3 Procedure 3: Titration of Salts as Base

Amine hydrohalides, nitrates and some sulfates, phosphates and citrates can be titrated by this procedure. Many sodium salts of inorganic acids have also been titrated.[2]

Reagents

0.1 M Perchloric acid in dioxane. (See Procedure 1.)
Crystal-violet or methyl-violet indicator. (See Procedure 1.)
Mercuric acetate. Dissolve 6 g of mercuric acetate in 100 ml of hot glacial acetic acid, and cool to room temperature.

Electrodes

General-purpose glass indicator electrode, calomel, or modified silver–silver chloride reference electrode (see p. 124).

Dissolve a sample containing from 0.3 to 0.8 meq of titratable base in 30–40 ml of ACS grade glacial acetic acid. If necessary, heat to effect dissolution (Note 1); or first dissolve the sample in a minimum of water (2 ml or less), and then add the acetic acid. If the sample is the hydrohalide salt of a base, add 5 ml of mercuric acetate solution. Titrate potentiometrically with 0.1 M perchloric acid in dioxane (Note 2), taking the point of maximum slope as the end point.

Notes

1. Some samples must be put through a 100 to 200 mesh sieve and refluxed gently with acetic acid to be put into solution.
2. Most salts can be successfully titrated by 0.1 M perchloric acid in acetic acid.

8.4 Procedure 4: Titration of Very Weak Bases in Acetic Anhydride Solvent Mixtures

This procedure may be used for titration of tertiary amines, aromatic heterocyclics, amine oxides, many salts, amides, sulfoxides, and phosphine oxides (See Refs. 14–26, Chap. 6). Primary and secondary amines cannot be titrated.

Reagents

>   0.1 M Perchloric acid in acetic acid. (See Procedure 1.)

Electrodes

>   General-purpose glass and calomel (fiber- or porous-plug type).

Procedure

>   Dissolve a sample containing from 0.3 to 0.8 meq of base in 4:1 v/v acetic anhydride-nitromethane (Note 1). Insert the electrodes, and titrate potentiometrically with 0.1 M perchloric acid in acetic acid (Note 2). Titrate a solvent blank to the same potential as the equivalence point in the main titration. Subtract this blank (usually 0.01–0.04 ml) from the buret reading.

Notes

>   **1.** Substances not soluble in this mixture may be dissolved first in a little acetic acid, heating if necessary to effect solution. If desired, pure acetic anhydride may be used instead of the nitromethane mixture. Acetic acid–acetic anhydride (4:1 v/v) may also be used, but the results are inferior to the nitromethane–acetic anhydride in some instances.

>   **2.** Trinitrobenzene sulfonic acid, instead of perchloric acid, is recommended for titration of primary amides.[3]

8.5   Procedure 5: Differentiating Titration of Base Mixtures

>   This procedure is applicable to the analysis of samples containing bases of different strength, such as mixtures containing an aliphatic amine and an aromatic amine, or an aromatic nitrogen heterocyclic compound. A ΔpK_b in H_2O of 2 or more is usually needed to resolve a mixture of two bases.

Reagents

>   0.1 M Perchloric acid in dioxane
>   Acetonitrile, reagent grade
>   Acetone, reagent grade

Electrodes

>   General-purpose glass indicator electrode
>   Calomel or silver–silver chloride reference electrode (see p. 124).

Procedure

Dissolve a sample containing from 0.5 to 1.0 meq of total base in 30 ml of acetonitrile or acetone (Note 1). Insert the electrodes, and titrate potentiometrically with 0.1 M perchloric acid in dioxane (Note 2). Plot the titration curve, and note the buret reading at each inflection. Also do a potentiometric blank titration on each batch of acetonitrile.

Calculations

Note the potential at each inflection of the sample titration, and find the buret readings of the blank that correspond to each of these potentials. Subtract these blank buret readings from the sample buret readings, and calculate the amount of each base.

> *Example*: Titration of a mixture of butylamine and pyridine gave an inflection for butylamine at a potential of 190 mv and a buret reading of 2.80 ml; the second inflection (pyridine) was at 485 mv and a buret reading of 6.54 ml. The buret readings of the solvent blank were 0.01 ml at 190 mv and 0.04 ml at 485 mv:
>
> $HClO_4$ to titrate butylamine = 2.80 − 0.01 = 2.79 ml.
> $HClO_4$ to titrate pyridine = 6.54 − 0.04 − 2.79 = 3.71 ml.

Notes

1. Acetone is less toxic and often has a lower basic blank than acetonitrile. However, some primary aliphatic amines reach equilibrium slowly in the titration region immediately preceding the equivalence point owing to Schiff's base formation with acetone. This difficulty is not encountered in acetonitrile.

2. Mixtures containing only weak bases with pK_b in $H_2O \geqq 9.0$ give somewhat better results if titrated in acetonitrile or in acetic acid with 0.1 M perchloric acid in acetic acid.

8.6   Procedure 6: Mixtures of Primary, Secondary, and Tertiary Amines[4]

Reagents

1 M Hydrochloric acid in ethylene glycol-2-propanol. Dilute 96 ml of conc. hydrochloric acid to 1 liter with a 1:1 mixture of ethylene glycol and 2-propanol. Standardize in terms of Procedure A, using *tris*(hydroxymethyl)aminomethane as the primary standard.

Salicylaldehyde (from bisulfite addition compound).

Electrodes

General-purpose glass indicator electrode. Calomel reference electrode.

Procedure A: Total Amines

Weigh accurately a sample containing approximately 20 meq of total amines into a 150-ml beaker (Note 1). Add 50 ml of 1:1 ethylene glycol-2-propanol. Titrate potentiometrically with 1 M hydrochloric acid in ethylene glycol-2-propanol, using either the millivolt or pH scale of a pH meter.

Procedure B: Secondary-Plus-Tertiary Amines

Weigh accurately a sample containing approximately 20 meq of secondary-plus-tertiary amines into a 150-ml beaker (Note 1). Add 50 ml of 1:1 ethylene glycol-2-propanol and 5 ml of salicylaldehyde (Note 2). Stir thoroughly, and allow to stand for 0.5 hour. Titrate potentiometrically with 1 M hydrochloric acid in ethylene glycol-2-propanol, using either the millivolt or pH scale of a pH meter (Note 3).

Procedure C: Tertiary Amines

Weigh accurately a sample containing approximately 20 meq of tertiary amines (Note 1) into a 20 x 150 mm test tube that has been cooled in a beaker of ice. Slowly add 20 ml of c.p. acetic anhydride, and swirl to mix. Let stand 15 min at room temperature (Note 4). Transfer quantitatively to a 150-ml beaker by washing with 1:1 ethylene glycol-2-propanol, and dilute to 50 ml with the same solvent mixture. Titrate potentiometrically with 1 M hydrochloric acid in ethylene glycol-2-propanol, using either the millivolt of pH scale of a pH meter.

Notes

1. This procedure is designed for use of a 50-ml buret.

2. More salicylaldehyde must be added if the sample contains more than 35 meq of primary amine.

3. The potentiometric end-point break is fairly sharp when the amines are aliphatic but quite gradual when a mixture of aromatic amines is analyzed.

4. This much time is sufficient for ordinary amines. Hindered amines, particularly secondary amines, may require a longer time and a higher temperature for acetylation.

Calculations

$$\% \ 1° \ \text{Amine} = 100 \ (\text{f. wt of amine}) \left[\frac{\text{mmoles total amine}}{\text{mg sample}} - \frac{\text{mmoles } 2° + 3°}{\text{mg sample}} \right]$$

$$\% \ 2° \ \text{Amine} = 100 \, (\text{f. wt of amines}) \left[\frac{\text{mmoles } 2° + 3°}{\text{mg sample}} - \frac{\text{mmoles } 3°}{\text{mg sample}} \right]$$

$$\% \ 3° \ \text{Amine} = 100 \, (\text{f. wt of amine}) \left[\frac{\text{mmoles } 3°}{\text{mg sample}} \right]$$

8.7   Procedure 7: Photometric Titration of Aromatic Amines

This procedure is adapted from Hummelstedt and Hume[5] and is designed exclusively for weak aromatic amines having a pK_b in H_2O from approximately 10 to 13.5. Mixtures of two amines can be resolved provided (1) and ΔpK_b in H_2O is $\geqslant 1.5$, and (2) a wavelength can be found where only the weaker base absorbs appreciably. Several examples are discussed by Hummelstedt and Hume.[5]

Reagents

Ordinary reagent-grade acetic acid is adequate for titration of bases up to $\sim pK_b$ in $H_2O = 12.5$. For weaker bases, add the calculated amount of acetic anhydride to combine with the water (Karl Fischer titration) and sulfuric acid catalyst, then distill the anhydrous reagent.

0.5 M Perchloric acid in acetic acid. Dilute 42 ml of 70–72% perchloric acid to 1 liter with glacial acetic acid. Standardize as in Procedure 1.

Apparatus

Beckman Model B, or another kind of spectrophotometer, with cell carriage removed to accommodate a 150-ml beaker or tallform beaker.[6] For titrations in the UV, use a 150-ml Vycor beaker grade 7910 (Corning Glass Works), transparent down to approximately 241 nm.

Procedure

Dissolve a sample containing from 0.5 to 2.5 meq of base in 100 ml of glacial acetic acid. Set the spectrophotometer to the desired wavelength (Note 1), and set the absorbance to zero using a pure solvent in the beaker (Note 2). Replace this beaker with the one containing the sample solution, and titrate with 0.5 M perchloric acid in acetic acid. Plot the absorbance readings vs. milliters of titrant. The end point(s) is(are) obtained by extrapolation of the straight-line portions of the titration curve.

Notes

1. The following wavelengths are given by Hummelstedt and Hume.[5]

Compound	λ, nm	Compound	λ, nm
2-Chloroaniline	320	N,N-Dimethyl-3-nitroaniline	518
4-Chloroaniline	327	N,N-Dimethyl-4-nitroaniline	485
2-Chloropyridine	294*	2-Methyl-5-nitroaniline	470
8-Chloroquinoline	380*	4-Methyl-2-nitroaniline	520
2,4-Dichloroaniline	335	3-Nitroaniline	464
2,5-Dichloroaniline	328	4-Nitroaniline	448

* Absorbance increases during titration.

2. For compounds where the absorbance increases, set the absorbance at zero with the sample solution in place.

8.8   Procedure 8: Determination of Epoxy Compounds

This procedure is adapted from Dijkstra and Dahmen.[7] The reaction is as follows (see p. 83):

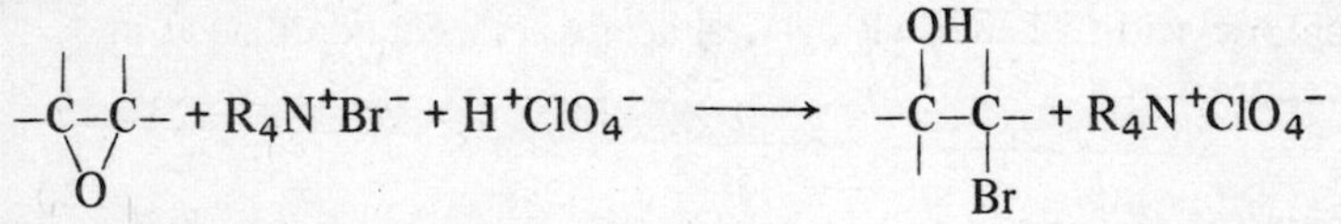

$$-\underset{\underset{O}{|}}{C}-\underset{|}{C}- + R_4N^+Br^- + H^+ClO_4^- \longrightarrow -\underset{|}{C}-\underset{\underset{Br}{|}}{C}- + R_4N^+ClO_4^-$$

(with OH on the product)

Reagents

0.1 M perchloric acid in glacial acetic acid (see Procedure 1).
Cetyltrimethylammonium bromide, commerical grade.
Crystal violet, 0.1% w/v in glacial acetic acid.
Glacial acetic acid, reagent grade.

Procedure

Weigh exactly a sample containing not more than 0.5 meq. of epoxide into a small flask or beaker. Add 25 ml of glacial acetic acid, 2 g of cetyltrimethylammonium bromide (Note 1), and 5 drops of crystal violet indicator. Stir magnetically, and titrate, immediately after dissolution of the solids, with 0.1 M perchloric acid in acetic acid to a bright green color.

Perform a blank titration exactly as described above, but omit the sample. The blank should not require more than 0.1–0.2 ml of titrant.

Note

1. Tetrabutylammonium iodide (1 g) may be used instead of the cetyltrimethylammonium bromide. Undoubtedly other quaternary ammonium bromides can also be used.

8.9 Procedure 9: Preparation and Standardization of Quaternary Ammonium Hydroxide Titrants

Tetrabutylammonium hydroxide can be purchased commerically either as a 0.1 *M* solution or as a more concentrated solution that can be diluted (Procedure A). This titrant usually contains weakly basic impurities. Quaternary ammonium hydroxide titrants of excellent purity can be prepared by ion exchange (Procedure B), which is a modification of the method originally proposed by Harlow, Noble, and Wyld.[8] The silver oxide method may also be used (Procedure C), but to obtain a pure titrant the purification steps outlined in this procedure must be followed.

Reagents

Amberlite A-26 anion exchange resin (Rohm and Haas). Grind, and sieve to 100–200 mesh.

Benzoic acid. Reagent or primary standard grade.

2-Propanol. Reagent grade. Remove dissolved carbon dioxide by bubbling nitrogen.

1 *M* sodium hydroxide, aqueous, carbonate-free.

Thymol blue. Dissolve 0.3 g in 100 ml of 2-propanol.

Tetrabutylammonium iodide. Reagent grade. Some batches require recrystallization (see below).

Tributylmethylammonium iodide. In a 250-ml flask equipped with a reflux condenser, mix 93 g (120 ml) of tributylamine and 75 g (35 ml) of methyl iodide. Cool the flask in ice when the reaction causes the flask to become hot. When the reaction is complete, dissolve the product in a minimum (the smallest volume that will dissolve the product) of boiling acetone. Cool; add anhydrous ether, and chill in an ice bath. Reprecipitate the crystals 3 or 4 times in acetone/ether, until the supernatant liquid is clear and the water white. Dry the product in the air and then in a desiccator.

Tetrabutylammonium hydroxide, 25% solution in methanol, (Eastman No. 7774).

Apparatus

Glass ion-exchange column. A tube from 2 to 4 cm in diameter or a 250-ml cylindrical separatory funnel would be satisfactory. The resin is supported by a glass frit or a plug of glass wool. Solutions are added to the column through a large separatory funnel or a similar reservoir.

Procedure A: Tetrabutylammonium Hydroxide (Commercial Titrant)

Dilute 100 g of 25% tetrabutylammonium hydroxide in methanol to 1 liter with 2-propanol. This gives a solution that would be approximately 0.1 M. Store in an automatic buret (protected from CO_2) or in a stoppered bottle under nitrogen. To standardize, weigh accurately benzoic acid samples of approximately 75 mg each. Dissolve these in approximately 25 ml of 2-propanol; add thymol blue indicator; and titrate under nitrogen with tetrabutylammonium hydroxide to the first permanent blue color. Titrate a separate blank, and subtract from the milliliters used in the standardizing titration.

Procedure B: Ion-Exchange Preparation of Tetrabutylammonium or Tributylmethylammonium Hydroxide

Slurry 50 g of air-dried anion exchange resin in distilled water, and add it to the column. Convert the resin to the hydroxyl form by passing 1 liter of 1 M sodium hydroxide through the column at a flow rate of not more than 10 ml/min. Rinse the column with boiled distilled water until the effluent is no longer basic. Then remove the water from the column by passing through 1.2 liters of 2-propanol at a flow rate of approximately 5 ml/min. Add 1 liter of a 2-propanol solution containing either 35 g/liter of tributylmethylammonium iodide or 40 g/liter tetrabutylammonium iodide (Note 1) to the column reservoir. Adjust the flow rate to 2-5 ml/min. As soon as the column effluent becomes basic (thymol blue turns blue), put the 1-liter receiver bottle in place (Note 2). Standardize the titrant against benzoic acid as outlined in Procedure A (Note 3).

Notes

1. Tributylmethylammonium hydroxide was found to be somewhat more stable on storage than tetrabutylammonium hydroxide; however, either one can perform very satisfactorily as a titrant. Titrants that are not expected to be used up within 2-3 weeks should be stored in a refrigerator.

2. The ion-exchange conversion of iodide to hydroxide may be carried out unattended if desired. The receiver should be protected from carbon dioxide in the atmosphere by passing a slow stream of nitrogen over it.

3. A titrant strength less than about 0.09 M probably indicates incomplete ion exchange, but this does not adversely affect the quality of the titrant. A slower flow rate should be used on the next batch.

Procedure C: Silver Oxide Preparation of Tetrabutylammonium Hydroxide.[9]

Slurry 23 g of purified silver oxide with 130 ml of a 75% methanol-25% water solution in an ice bath at 0°C. Add, slowly, 32 g of tetrabutylammonium bromide (Note 1) in 35 ml of pure methanol; and stir from 10 to 15 minutes. Filter the base solution through a coarse sintered glass frit into a flask containing 0.5 g of activated charcoal; mix well; and allow it to settle for several hours. Filter the base solution through a fine sintered glass frit into a flask containing a magnetic stirring bar. Remove the methanol by evaporation at a pressure of 25 torr. Transfer the aqueous solution to a 250-ml graduated addition funnel, and dilute to 200 ml with boiled distilled water. Add from 30 to 40 ml of pure benzene; shake vigorously; and let the two phases separate completely. Pass the aqueous solution through a column containing from 8 to 10 grams of strong base anion exchange resin in the hydroxide formed. When titrant is needed, distill water from the crystalline hydrate until the vapor pressure is between 7 and 10 torr. The resulting solution will be approximately $2M$. Dilute it to 1 liter with a mixture of 20% 2-propanol-80% benzene. (Note 2).

Notes

1. If desired, 35 g of tributylmethylammonium iodide or 40 g of tetrabutylammonium iodide may be used.

2. Dilution with 2-propanol alone is also satisfactory.

8.10   Procedure 10: Titration of Acids

Compounds that have an acidic strength such that pK_b in $H_2O \geqq 11$ can be titrated by any one of the procedures given (see Chap. 7).

Reagents

0.1 M Tributylmethylammonium hydroxide or tetrabutyl-ammonium hydroxide. (See Procedure 9.)

Azo violet. Dissolve 0.2 g of p-nitrobenzeneazoresorcinol in 100 ml of 2-propanol, heating to hasten solution.

Thymol blue. Dissolve 0.3 g. of thymol blue in 100 ml of 2-propanol or methanol.

Solvents

Use one of the following reagent grade solvents.

Compound	Suggested solvent
Carboxylic acids	Acetone, t-butyl alcohol, dimethylformamide, 2-propanol, or pyridine.
Dicarboxylic acids	2-Propanol, dimethylformamide
Enols, imides	Dimethylformamide, acetone
Nitro compounds	Pyridine
Phenols	t-Butyl alcohol, acetone, dimethylformamide, pyridine.
Strong acids	2-Propanol, t-butyl alcohol, pyridine
Sulfonamides	Dimethylformamide

Electrodes

General-purpose glass indicator electrode.

Calomel or silver–silver chloride reference electrode (see p. 124).

Procedure A: Total Acid

Dissolve a sample containing from 0.3 to 0.8 meq. of acid in 30–40 ml of a suitable solvent. Add from 1 to 2 drops of thymol-blue or azo-violet indicator (Note 1); insert a glass indicator electrode and a reference electrode. Under nitrogen, titrate potentiometrically with 0.1 M tributyl-methylammonium hydroxide or tetrabutylammonium hydroxide. Note the indicator color change that corresponds with the potentiometric end point. Subsequent titrations of similar samples may be made using this indicator color (Note 2). Titrate a solvent blank to the same potential (or indicator color) as the sample end point, and subtract this blank from the volume of titrant used to titrate the acid sample.

Procedure B: Acid Mixtures

Dissolve a sample containing from 0.3 to 0.8 meq. of total acid in 30–40 ml of t-butyl alcohol or dimethylformamide. Insert a glass and a reference electrode. Titrate potentiometrically under nitrogen with 0.1 M tributylmethylammonium hydroxide or tetrabutylammonium hydroxide.

Plot the titration curve, and note the buret reading at each inflection. Titrate a solvent blank to the potential of each sample end point, and subtract the blank at each end point from the appropriate sample buret reading.

Procedure C: Salts*

Test the sample for solubility in dimethylformamide. If it is not completely soluble, dissolve it in a minimum of water (1-2 drops) and dilute with 95-100% ethylenediamine. Dissolve a salt sample containing from 0.3-0.8 meq. of tltratable acid in 15-25 ml of dimethylformamide or water-ethylene-diamine. Add from 1 to 2 drops of thymol-blue or azo-violet indicator (Note 3), and titrate under nitrogen to the first permanent blue color. Titrate a solvent blank under the same conditions, and subtract from the sample buret reading.[9]

Notes

1. Thymol blue is satisfactory to use for strong to moderately weak acids; azo violet should be used for weak acids.

2. For indicator titrations the amount of solvent can be reduced to 15-25 ml.

3. Use thymol blue in dimethylformamide and azoviolet in water-ethylenediamine.

8.11   Procedure 11: Coulometric Titration of Acids[10]

Reagents

Azoviolet. Dissolve 0.2 g in 100 ml of 2-propanol, with heating.

t-Butyl alcohol. Reagent grade, purified by redistillation.

2-Nitroaniline. Dissolve 0.3 g in 100 ml of 2-propanol.

Tetrabutylammonium bromide. Polarographic grade.

Tetramethylammonium bromide. Reagent grade.

Apparatus

Sargent Model IV coulometric current source or similar constant-current source.

Titration cell as shown in Fig. 7.6, p. 111. The anode and cathode are made of sheet platinum, approximately 20 cm^2 in area. The anode and cathode compartments are separated by an anion-exchange membrane (Nepton 111BZL065 from Ionics, Inc., Cambridge, Mass.).

---

* Adapted from J. S. Fritz, *Anal. Chem.*, **24** (1952), p. 306.

Procedure

Add ∼15 ml of 0.1 *M* tetrabutylammonium bromide in *t*-butyl alcohol and several drops of the appropriate indicator to the cathode compartment (Note 1). Add an equal volume of 0.1 *M* tetramethylammonium bromide in methanol to the anode compartment. Set the cell cover and generating electrodes in place, and bubble a slow stream of nitrogen through the cathode solution to purge it of dissolved carbon dioxide. With a slow stream of nitrogen passing over the cathode solution and with the magnetic stirrer on, generate the titrant at the 0.005 setting (∼5 mA), 0.01 setting, or 0.02 setting until the indicator changes color. Then add the sample, and titrate it to the same color change using the same setting to generate the titrant base. Calculate the amount of acid present from the number of coulombs passed, after subtracting the blank.

Note

1. Azo violet is satisfactory to use for titration of most acids. Weakly acidic phenols require 2-nitroaniline indicator.

REFERENCES

1. E. B. Buchanen, Jr., *Talanta*, **13** (1964), 1599.
2. C. W. Pifer and E. G. Wollish, *Anal. Chem.*, **24** (1952), 519.
3. D. J. Pietrzyk, *Anal. Chem.*, **39** (1967), 1367.
4. S. Siggia, J. G. Hanna, and I. B. Kervenski, *Anal. Chem.*, **22** (1950), 1295.
5. L. E. I. Hummelstedt and D. N. Hume, *Anal. Chem.*, **32** (1960), 576.
6. J. S. Fritz and D. J. Pietrzyk, *Anal. Chem.*, **31** (1959), 1157.
7. R. Dijkstra and E. A. M. F. Dahmen, *Anal. Chim. Acta*, **31** (1964), 38.
8. G. A. Harlow, C. M. Noble, and G. E. A. Wyld, *Anal. Chem.*, **28** (1956), 787.
9. L. W. Marple and J. S. Fritz, *Anal. Chem.*, **34** (1962), 796.
10. J. S. Fritz and F. E. Gainer, *Talanta*, **15** (1968), 939.

INDEX

NOTES

NOTES

NOTES